THE ECONOMIC DEMAND FOR IRRIGATED ACREAGE

New Methodology and Some Preliminary Projections, 1954-1980

THE ECONOMIC DEMAND FOR IRRIGATED ACREAGE

New Methodology and Some Preliminary Projections, 1954–1980

by VERNON W. RUTTAN

Published for RESOURCES FOR THE FUTURE, INC.

by THE JOHNS HOPKINS PRESS, Baltimore, Maryland

Library of Congress Catalog Card Number 65–13930

RESOURCES FOR THE FUTURE, INC.
1755 Massachusetts Avenue, N.W., Washington, D.C. 20036

Resources for the Future is a non-profit corporation for research and education in the development, conservation, and use of natural resources. It was established in 1952 with the co-operation of the Ford Foundation and its activities since then have been financed by grants from that Foundation. Part of the work of Resources for the Future is carried out by its resident staff, part supported by grants to universities and other non-profit organizations. Unless otherwise stated, interpretations and conclusions in RFF publications are those of the authors; the organization takes responsibility for the selection of significant subjects for study, the competence of the researchers, and their freedom of inquiry.

This study by Vernon W. Ruttan, professor of agricultural economics at Purdue University, was supported by an RFF grant to Purdue Research Foundation. Mr. Ruttan is currently on leave from the university and serving as agricultural economist with the International Rice Research Institute in the Philippines. This book is part of RFF's water research program, directed by Allen V. Kneese.

RFF Publications Staff: Henry Jarrett, *editor;* Vera W. Dodds, *associate editor;* Nora E. Roots, *assistant editor.*

FOREWORD

In a country as richly endowed with water resources as the United States the task of water resource management and development should be influenced less by fears of absolute water shortage than by concern over excessive use for some purposes which serve to inhibit or exclude other more valuable uses. As a general proposition, a resource should be employed in a given application to the extent that the value of its output at the margin exceeds its cost; its use should be curtailed if costs associated with its employment exceed the value of its contribution in production. Estimates of the marginal value productivity of water in alternative applications in the several supply regions, therefore, are essential for the prudent management of existing supplies—and as guides to the level, rate, and character of development of new supplies. Although this is a truism in elementary economics, its implementation in the water field has been greatly delayed by reason of the unique complexity encountered in this area.

Because of the cost of transporting large amounts of fresh water over long distances, there is no national market for water as there is for farm and forest products, fuels, and metals. Thus, long-range projections of national availability and use are of limited utility for water. Not until 1960 was there a systematic effort to appraise the national outlook on the basis of an analysis of individual regions. This work was done under the auspices of the Senate Select Committee on National Water Resources in a study directed by Nathaniel Wollman of the University of New Mexico while he was a temporary member of the staff of Resources for the Future. Results were presented in Committee Print No. 32, "Water Resources Activities in the United States," which set forth projections of water use in twenty-two regions and compared them with available supplies.

Projections of this kind, which are based on the quantity of inputs "required" to support some projected level of output, are useful for pointing up potential scarcities and possible conflicts. But for some purposes—particularly the planning of water development, with its need for long-range public and private investment—a wider range of alternatives should be taken into account.

In this pioneering work, Vernon Ruttan takes a long step toward meeting this deficiency. His approach is a significant departure from traditional projection efforts. The flexibility of his "elasticity" framework permits exploration of the implications of alternative resource and locational combinations in achieving a given food and fiber production objective not possible in the traditional approaches. Bringing into play the possibilities for substitution among resources and regions permits economic analysis and projection efforts to play their most productive role in illuminating the range of choice for policy decisions. Ruttan reveals, for example, that land and water development in the subhumid East represents an economical substitute for extension of submarginal irrigation in some of the more arid regions of the West where other uses of water would have higher value.

The significance of this study lies more perhaps in the framework of analysis than in the particular empirical results. There remains much room for more intensive analyses by individual scholars in the several water resource regions to further improve the quality of the estimates and increase the precision of the results. Thus, while the task may be unfinished in this respect, this study is being published in the hope that, among other results, it may serve to stimulate intensive regional efforts along these lines.

JOHN V. KRUTILLA
December, 1964 *Resources for the Future, Inc.*

ACKNOWLEDGMENTS

This report is based on work conducted under Purdue Agricultural Experiment Station Project 917 and was financed by a grant from Resources for the Future, Inc.

The research reported here draws heavily on two earlier studies: (1) J. C. Headley, "The Contribution of Supplemental Irrigation to Agricultural Output in Eastern United States" (Ph.D. thesis, Purdue University, Department of Agricultural Economics, January, 1960). This research was also financed by the grant from Resources for the Future. (2) V. W. Ruttan, "The Impact of Irrigation on Farm Output in California," *Hilgardia,* Vol. 31, No. 4, University of California, Berkeley, 1961, pp. 69–111. The California work, conducted while I was on leave at the Giannini Foundation of Agricultural Economics at the University of California, was financed by the California Water Resources Center.

For counsel and guidance in formulating and conducting the project I am particularly indebted to Christoph Beringer, Organisation for Economic Cooperation and Development, Paris (formerly at Giannini Foundation of Agricultural Economics, University of California), J. C. Headley, Department of Agricultural Economics, University of Illinois; Glenn L. Johnson, Department of Agricultural Economics, Michigan State University; Earl W. Kehrberg, Department of Agricultural Economics, Purdue University; Ivan M. Lee, Giannini Foundation of Agricultural Economics, University of California; G. E. Schuh, Department of Agricultural Economics, Purdue University; G. S. Tolley, Department of Agricultural Economics, North Carolina State of the University of North Carolina at Raleigh; S. V. Ciriacy-Wantrup, Giannini Foundation of Agricultural Economics, University of California; Nathaniel Wollman, Department of Economics, University of New Mexico; and Irving K. Fox, Allen V. Kneese, and John V. Krutilla, Resources for the Future.

VERNON W. RUTTAN

CONTENTS

LIST OF TEXT TABLES

LIST OF FIGURES

1

INTRODUCTION

Economists have long been concerned by the fact that projections of resource use have been made on the basis of the quantity of inputs "required" to support some projected level of final output. Projections of water use, as well as of other natural resources, have uniformly had this characteristic. The "requirement" is ordinarily determined by applying a factor or coefficient to a projected level of output. Such coefficients are ordinarily obtained from an existing relationship, possibly adjusted for trend in some manner. The difficulty with such projections is that they cannot encompass the tremendous capacity of the economy to adjust to changes in the availability and cost of resources. Requirements projections implicitly assume that the projected amount of the input will be used regardless of the costs of supplying it.

Projections of water use derived in this fashion imply that regional shifts in the location of production and adjustments in technique in response to the costs of using water are impossible. In the extreme, such projections may imply use of a greater amount of water than is physically available in the region. When this occurs, problems of allocation and efficient use are pointed up in particularly stark form. Indeed, one of the useful purposes of requirements projections can be to identify such conflicts. By their very nature, however, they do not provide a basis for evaluating outputs associated with particular increments of water use, and therefore provide no basis for determining how to achieve an efficient allocation. If projections of demand are to be used as the basis for general judgments of the justifiability of making investments to augment supplies, functions which relate demand to cost are essential.

This study concentrates on the economic demand for irrigation. While this is only one type of water use, it is nevertheless an exceedingly important one. In the western United States, still upwards of 90 per cent of all water use is for irrigation purposes. Since irrigation is the most consumptive of water uses, an even higher percentage of total water losses is accounted for by this activity. Moreover, there are continuing large programs for further investment in irrigation by the federal government. In some areas conflicts between irrigation water use and other water uses have already developed. In such instances it is particularly urgent that plans for further irrigation reflect the actual economic demand for water in this use. The rapid growth and concentration of population will bring increased competition for water for urban and industrial uses.

The objective of this study is to provide a method for determining the economic demand for irrigation—one that can be used to estimate the relative profitability of public and private investment in irrigation development on a broad regional basis, and that can provide an improved basis for public decisions on water projects.

Chapter 2 reviews the changing role of land, including irrigated land, in the growth of agricultural output in the United States, and points up the limitations of the requirements approach in projecting the use of agricultural inputs.

Chapter 3 contains a detailed exposition of the two elasticity models utilized to estimate regional resource productivity levels and to project regional output growth. These are constructed to permit the introduction of "optimization" rather than "requirements" criteria, and to permit substitution relationships among inputs and between inputs and outputs. In one, output growth in each region is determined from outside the system; in the other, regional output levels are determined simultaneously along with irrigated land and other input levels.

In Chapter 4 the models are used to relate the cost and productivity of irrigated acreage in the nation's major resource regions under recent conditions. A comparison of the cost and productivity estimates indicates the profitability of future investment, and they serve as a guide to the direction of future change.

In Chapter 5 alternative projections of national and regional farm output and irrigated acreage are derived from the models and then compared with the projections prepared for the Senate Select Committee on National Water Resources by the U.S. Department of Agriculture and by the U.S. Bureau of Reclamation. The comparisons show that the inclusion of substitution possibilities of various kinds leads to substantial differences. It must be mentioned that the estimates made here are based on rather gross data, which in some instances put a considerable strain on the methodology. The actual numbers projected should be taken as illustrative and the best that could be produced without considerably more detailed data collection and information about the regions.

This point is emphasized in Chapter 6 which evaluates the advantages and limitations of the elasticity models, summarizes the empirical results, and discusses the implications of this study for irrigation policy.

2

RESOURCE UTILIZATION IN AMERICAN AGRICULTURE

The conviction that the requirements approach to resource projections is becoming progressively less adequate is reinforced by the changes that have been taking place in American agriculture.

Of particular significance is the output explosion of the 1950's. During the early years of the decade discussion centered on the problem of how to meet the future requirements of a growing population. The President's Water Resources Policy Commission warned that the equivalent of 100 million acres of cropland would have to be added to meet the 1975 demand for farm output,[1] and stated that approximately two-thirds of this increase would have to come from resource development activities such as irrigation, flood protection, drainage, and land clearing, if American farmers were to fill what the U.S. Department of Agriculture referred to as the "fifth plate."[2] By 1961 the nation's farmers had already filled the "fifth plate" and were well on their way toward filling a sixth.

Farm output rose from an index of 101 in 1950 (1947–49=100) to an index of 124 in 1961. This increase—the largest of any decade since the turn of the century—was brought about by increased productivity. The change that took place was not in acreage of agricultural land but in the relationship between land and other resources employed in production and between farm output and total resource inputs.

[1] President's Water Resources Policy Commission, *Water Policy for the American People,* Vol. I (Washington: U.S. Government Printing Office, 1952), pp. 156–59.

[2] U.S. Department of Agriculture, *The Fifth Plate* (Washington, December, 1951).

RESOURCE INPUTS AND TECHNOLOGICAL CHANGE

Increases in farm output flow from two basic sources—increases in the physical inputs or resources used in production and increases in the efficiency or the productivity with which these resources are employed.[3] During the decade of the 1950's the entire increase in farm output was accounted for by increased productivity (Table 1). Total resource inputs have remained almost unchanged since 1950.

TABLE 1. Annual Average Rates of Change in Total Output, Inputs, and Productivity in U. S. Agriculture, 1870–1961

(Per cent/year)

Item	1870–1900	1900–25	1925–50	1950–61
Farm output	2.9	0.9	1.5	2.0
Total inputs	1.9	1.1	0.3	0.0
Total productivity	1.0	−0.2	1.2	2.0
Labor inputs [1]	1.6	0.5	−1.8	−4.2
Labor productivity	1.3	0.4	3.3	6.5
Land inputs [2]	3.1	0.8	0.1	−0.9
Land productivity	−0.2	0.0	1.4	2.8

[1] Number of workers, 1870–1910; man-hour basis, 1910–61.
[2] Cropland used for crops, including crop failure and cultivated summer fallow.

Sources: Computed from U.S. Department of Agriculture, *Changes in Farm Production and Efficiency*, Statistical Bulletin 223 (revised), Washington, September, 1962; and D. D. Durost and G. T. Barton, *Changing Sources of Farm Output*, U.S. Department of Agriculture, Production Research Report No. 36, Washington, February, 1960.

This experience of the last decade stands in sharp contrast to earlier experience in U.S. agriculture (see Table 1). Between 1870 and 1900 almost two-thirds of the increase in output was accounted for by increased inputs. With resource inputs expanding by 1.9 per cent per year

[3] Attempts to determine the source of the rising productivity indicate that technological change and education have played important roles over the longer run. Other factors such as economies of scale, closer approximation to firm and industry equilibrium, and regional and firm specialization have also been suggested. For an evaluation of the research on this issue, see V. W. Ruttan, "Research on the Economics of Technological Change in American Agriculture," *Journal of Farm Economics,* Vol. 42 (November, 1960), pp. 743–46.

and output per unit of gross inputs expanding at 1.0 per cent per year, output rose by 2.9 per cent per year. Between 1900 and 1925 resource inputs grew by only 1.1 per cent per year. This relatively slow rate of growth in resource inputs together with an actual decline in productivity combined to produce a growth in farm output of less than one per cent per year. In the quarter century between 1925 and 1950 the rate of increase in utilization of resource inputs slowed to 0.3 per cent per year, but a rise in the level of productivity to 1.2 per cent per year permitted an output expansion of 1.5 per cent per year. By the 1950 decade productivity was increasing at a sufficiently rapid rate to account for the entire increase in farm output.

From the standpoint of national resource policy the lag in agricultural productivity during the first quarter of this century is particularly important. This is the only period since 1870 which experienced a sustained increase in agricultural prices relative to the general price level. With the application of new technology proceeding only fast enough to offset the effect of diminishing returns, even relatively rapid price increases were not sufficient to draw additional resources into agricultural production fast enough to maintain a rate of agricultural output growth equal to the rate of population growth. The implications of lagging productivity and resource development during this period were brought to the attention of legislators and consumers through the mechanism of rising food prices.

The public concern with resource policy generated during this period led to increased emphasis on conservation and development of physical resources and increased allocation of public funds for research and education designed to speed the rate of technological change in American agriculture. The success of these policies has clearly demonstrated that it is possible to regard technological change and resource investment as partial substitutes for each other in achieving increased agricultural output. The objective of agricultural resource development now goes beyond simply assuring that the nation will be able to meet expanding food and fiber requirements. The aim is to meet these needs with the most efficient combination of expenditures on resource conservation and development and of expenditures on activities leading to technological change and increased productivity at each level of output.

CHANGES IN RESOURCE COMBINATIONS

The changes in resource combinations used in producing the nation's increased farm output have been equally as dramatic as the changing relationship between total resource inputs, productivity, and farm output. While total inputs remained approximately unchanged between 1950 and 1960, sharp changes were occurring among the individual input components (Figure 1).

Capital investment, particularly in the form of mechanical power and machinery, has continued its long-term rise. Even though the rate of increase leveled off during the late 1950's, the input of machinery and equipment in 1961 was 39 per cent above the 1947–49 level. Inputs of current operating expenses, of which fertilizer is a major component, rose even more rapidly, and by 1961 farmers were using almost twice

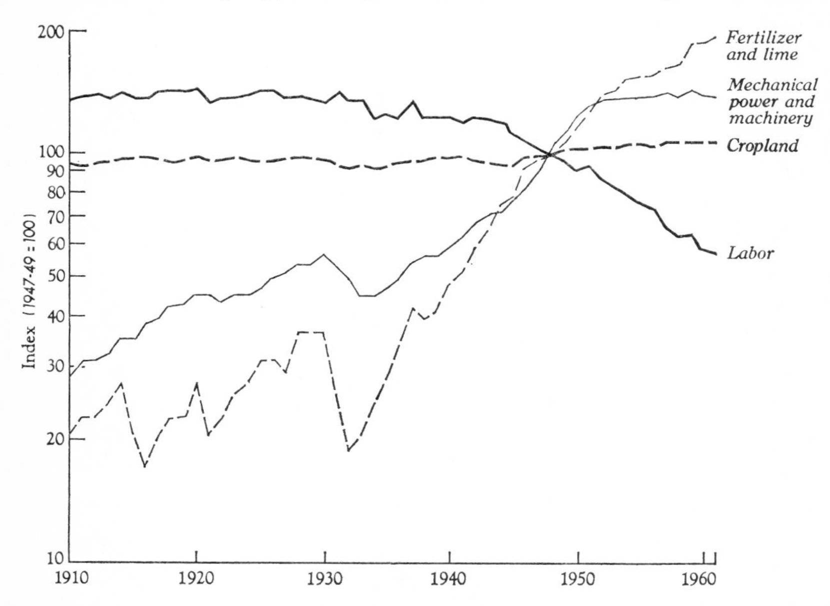

FIGURE 1. Indexes of Changes in Major Input Components in U.S. Agriculture, 1910–61. (Source: U.S. Department of Agriculture, *Changes in Farm Production and Efficiency,* Statistical Bulletin No. 233 [rev.], Washington, September, 1962, pp. 49–50.)

as much fertilizer as in 1947–49. Labor inputs, however, declined. After remaining virtually unchanged between 1910 and 1930, they began to drop sharply after the mid-1930's, and by 1961 were more than 40 per cent below the 1947–49 level.

Cropland used for crop production rose to an all-time peak of slightly above 380 million acres in the early 1930's, remained near this level until the soil bank program was initiated in 1954, and declined to 340 million acres in 1961. In spite of this relative stability in aggregate land inputs, sizable changes have occurred in the regional distribution of land use. Cropland acreage declined sharply in the Northeast and in the South, and increased substantially in the Corn Belt, Northern Plains, and the Mountain and Pacific regions.

The changes in resource combinations in recent years have been in response to changes in both technical coefficients and factor prices. The dramatic rise in the use of fertilizer is clearly a response to the fact that fertilizer prices have risen less than the index of prices paid by farmers while land prices have risen more rapidly (Table 2). The most striking feature about agricultural development in the United States is not its stability but the way in which it responds to economic and technological changes in spite of the role of the federal government in both product and factor markets.

TABLE 2. Changes in Quantities of Inputs per Unit of Total U. S. Farm Output and Changes in Prices of Inputs by Type of Input, 1940–60

(1960 as a per cent of 1940)

Input	Input per unit of farm output	Price per unit of input
Man-hours	33	[1] 495
Cropland	62	[2] 351
Tractors	195	[3] 249
Fertilizer	276	156
All inputs	68	[4] 217

[1] Farm wage rates.
[2] Value of farm land per acre with improvements.
[3] Farm machinery price index.
[4] All commodities bought for use in production.

Sources: Karl A. Fox, V. W. Ruttan, and L. W. Witt, *Farming, Farmers and Markets for Farm Goods,* Committee for Economic Development (Washington, November, 1962), p. 36; and U.S. Department of Agriculture, *Agricultural Statistics, 1961* (Washington: U.S. Government Printing Office, 1962).

THE GROWTH OF IRRIGATION

In the two decades from 1939 to 1959 the acreage of irrigated land in the continental United States almost doubled, rising from just under 18.0 million acres in 1939 to 25.8 million acres in 1949 and 33.0 million acres in 1959. In the western water resource regions, irrigated acreage expanded from approximately 17.6 million acres in 1939 to 31.1 million acres in 1959. In the eastern water resource regions it increased from under 400,000 acres in 1939 to over 2 million acres in 1954 and then dropped back to about 1.9 million acres in 1959 (Figure 2).

Estimates based on work by Durost and Barton indicate that increases in irrigated acreage accounted for between 5 and 8 per cent of the growth in farm output between 1940 and 1960.[4] Another indication of the impact of irrigation expansion on agricultural output is that the 7.2 million acres of irrigated land brought into production between 1949 and 1959 were roughly equivalent in productive capacity to the 25–30 million acres taken out of agricultural production during this same period for nonfarm use and by the acreage allotment and soil bank programs.[5]

The projections by the Department of Agriculture and the Bureau of Reclamation for the Senate Select Committee on Water Resources indicate that the expansion achieved in recent years is expected to continue (Figure 2).[6] Sharply different growth patterns have been experienced,

[4] D. D. Durost and G. T. Barton, *Changing Sources of Farm Output,* U.S. Department of Agriculture, Production Research Report No. 36 (Washington, February, 1960), p. 21; Karl A. Fox, V. W. Ruttan, and L. W. Witt, *Farming, Farmers and Markets for Farm Goods,* Committee for Economic Development (Washington, November, 1962), p. 34.

[5] V. W. Ruttan, "Our Growing Farm Output Potential," *Economic and Marketing Information for Indiana Farmers* (Lafayette, Indiana: Purdue University, January 29, 1960), pp. 2–4.

[6] U.S. Department of Agriculture, *Land and Water Potentials and Future Requirements for Water* (Committee Print No. 12), and U.S. Bureau of Reclamation, *Future Needs for Reclamation in the Western States* (Committee Print No. 14), U.S. Senate Select Committee on National Water Resources (Washington: U.S. Government Printing Office, 1960). The Bureau projections were developed by adding the acres of newly irrigated land included in potential projects (p. 11) to Bureau estimates of irrigated acreage in 1958 (p. 3). The potential projections clearly exceed the levels likely to be realized by either 1980 or 2000. The Bureau does not, however, present in Committee Print No. 14 the acreage of new land to be irrigated in western water resource regions by 1980 or 2000; the projections on page 19 are on a "new land equivalent" basis which includes an adjustment for supplemental water provided for presently irrigated land.

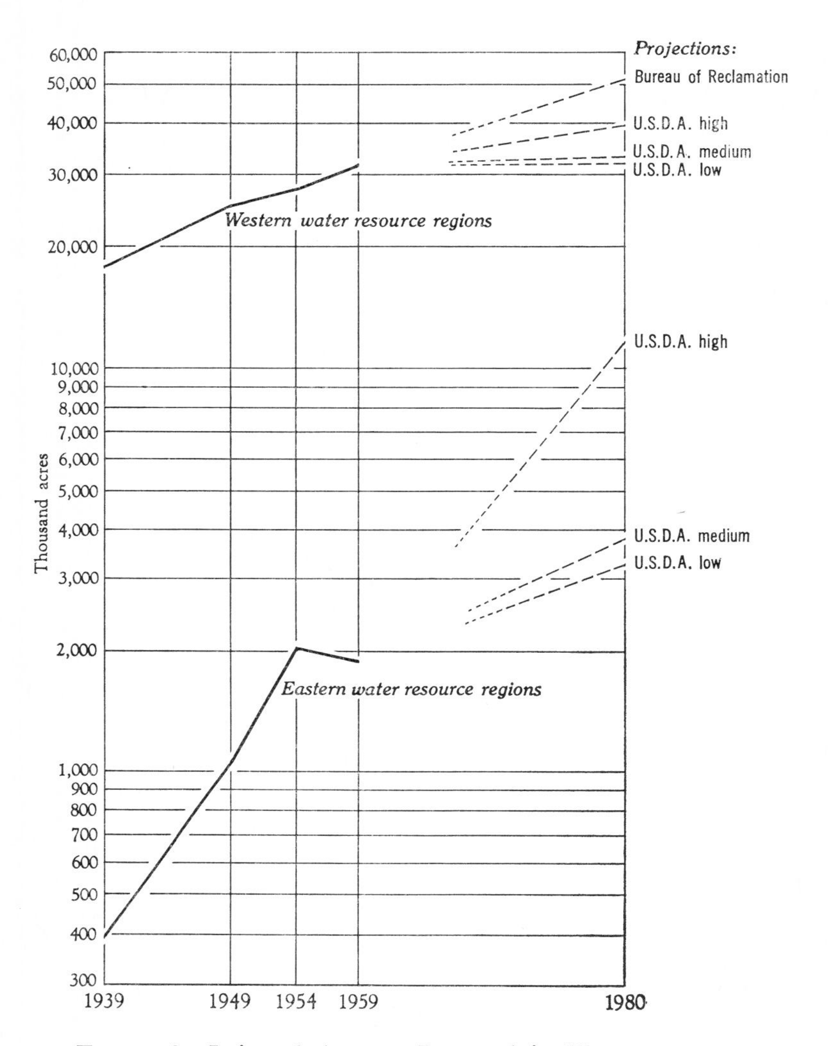

FIGURE 2. Irrigated Acreage Reported in Western and Eastern Water Resource Regions for 1939, 1949, 1954, and 1959, and Projections to 1980 by the U.S. Department of Agriculture and Bureau of Reclamation.

and are anticipated, among individual water resource regions in both major areas (Figures 3 and 4; also Table 17).

In the three Pacific regions, irrigated acreage expanded rapidly prior to 1954. After 1954, however, irrigated acreage expanded somewhat more slowly in the Central Pacific and declined slightly in the South Pacific region.

Among the three Southern Mountain areas irrigated acreage has continued to expand in recent years only in the Upper Rio Grande and Pecos region. The Great Basin experienced a decline in irrigated acreage

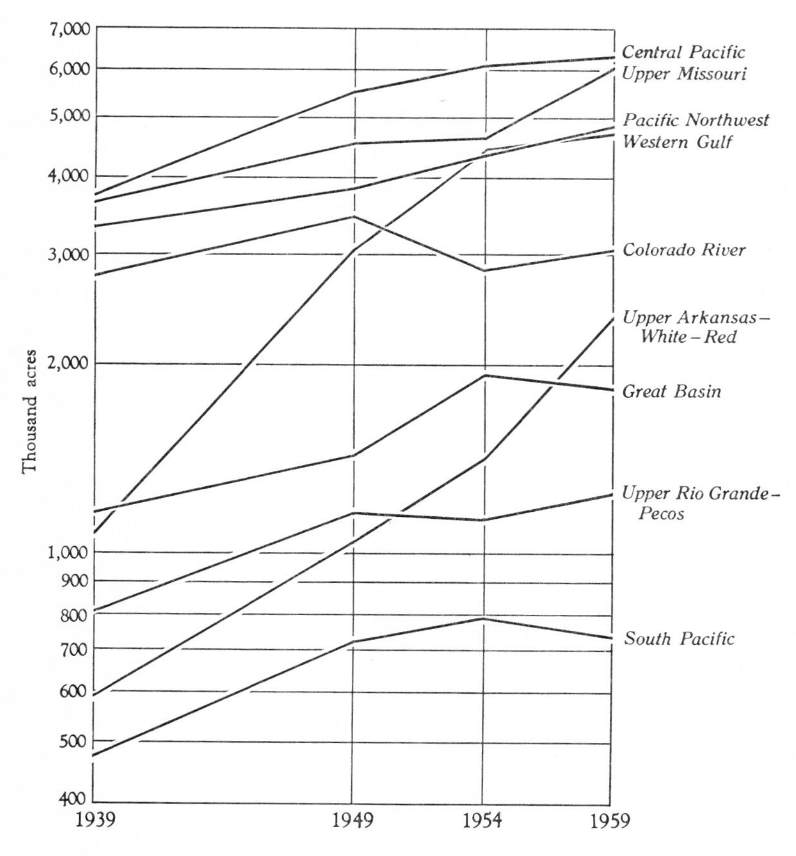

FIGURE 3. Irrigated Land in Western Water Resource Regions.

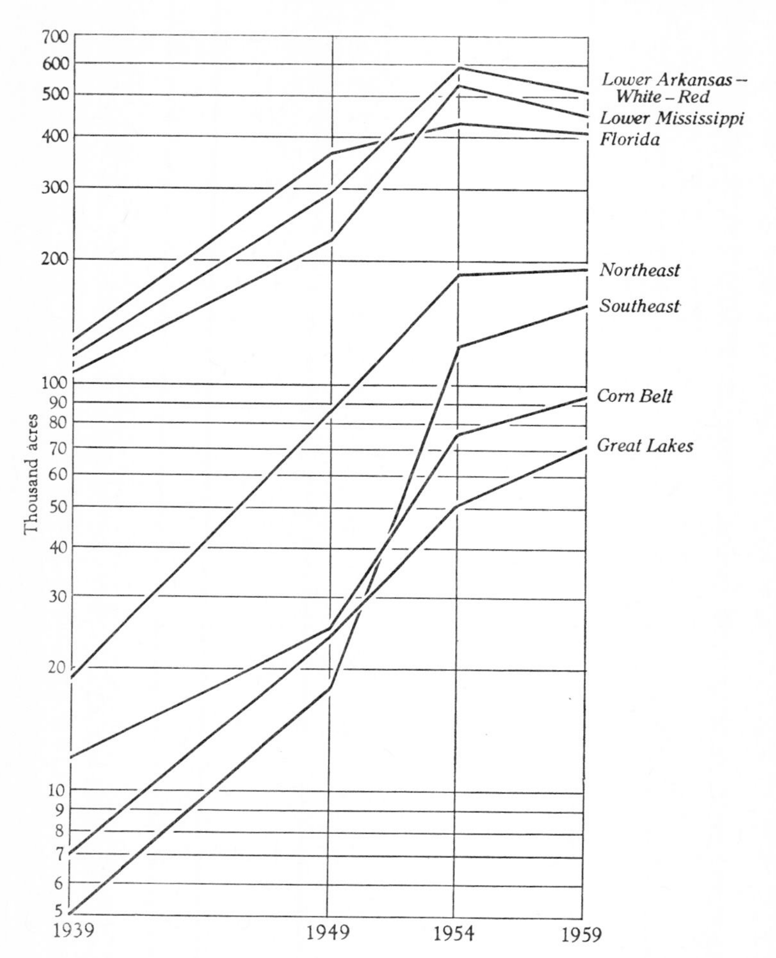

FIGURE 4. Irrigated Land in Eastern Water Resource Regions.

between 1954 and 1959, and in the Colorado River region irrigated acreage remains below the 1949 level in spite of a partial recovery between 1954 and 1959.

In each of the three water resource regions of the Great Plains—Upper Missouri, Upper Arkansas-White-Red rivers, and Western Gulf—irrigated acreage continued to expand sharply during the last decade.

The lag in expansion of irrigated acreage in the Central and South Pacific regions after 1954 appears to reflect near completion or lagging development of a number of projects started in the late 1930's and early 1940's. In the South Pacific region increased competition between irrigation and urban uses has also apparently been of some importance.[7]

In the Southern Mountain regions, limitations on water availability and competition from growing urban use, plus abnormally low water supplies during the middle 1950's, all seem to have interacted to limit irrigation expansion.

The rapid expansion of irrigated acreage in the three Great Plains regions appears to reflect recent development work on the Missouri and Arkansas-White-Red rivers plus a series of technological break-throughs which have reduced the cost of pumping and distributing water.[8]

The major expansion of irrigated acreage in the eastern water resource regions occurred prior to 1954. In the Florida, Lower Mississippi River, and Lower Arkansas-White-Red regions—the three regions which accounted for over 75 per cent of all acreage irrigated in the East—irrigated acreage declined between 1954 and 1959 (Figure 4). In the Northeast, Corn Belt, Great Lakes, and Southeast irrigated acreage continued to rise after 1954 but at a much lower rate than was achieved during the previous half decade.

It seems clear that somewhat different factors have been operating to bring about the changes in irrigated acreage in the several eastern water resource regions.[9] In the Lower Mississippi and Lower Arkansas-White-Red regions, the expansion of rice acreage and increased adoption of irrigation in cotton production were important factors in the ex-

[7] Jack Hirshleifer, J. C. DeHaven, and J. W. Milliman, *Water Supply: Economics, Technology and Policy* (Chicago: University of Chicago Press, 1960), pp. 289–95.

[8] Edward A. Ackerman and George O. G. Löf, *Technology in American Water Development* (Baltimore: The Johns Hopkins Press for Resources for the Future, 1959), pp. 270–84. Also M. M. Tharp and C. W. Crickman, "Supplemental Irrigation in Humid Areas," in *Water: The Yearbook of Agriculture, 1955* (Washington: U.S. Government Printing Office, 1955), pp. 252–58.

[9] See R. L. Tontz, "Future of Irrigation in the Humid Area," *Journal of Farm Economics,* Vol. 40 (August, 1958), pp. 636–52; and J. C. Headley, "Factors Associated with the Location of Supplemental Irrigation in the Humid Area," *Land Economics,* Vol. 37 (May, 1961), pp. 187–89.

pansion of irrigated acreage during the period prior to 1954. The decline in irrigated acreage after 1954 reflects the effect of acreage controls imposed during the latter half of the 1950's as surpluses of both cotton and rice continued to increase. The slight decline in irrigated acreage in Florida after 1954 reflects heavier rainfall during 1958 and 1959 than in the mid-1950's.[10]

The rapid expansion of irrigated acreage in the four other eastern water resource regions prior to 1954 appears to reflect the relatively high prices for agricultural products that prevailed prior to the sharp decline between 1952 and 1955; a series of technological developments which reduced the costs of sprinkler irrigation; and a number of relatively dry years in many parts of the humid area during the early 1950's. The dampening of the upward trend in irrigated acreage in these areas during the latter half of the 1950's reflects the effect of lower farm prices and more rainfall.[11]

Despite the rapid growth in recent years, irrigation development is extremely limited in the East—a fact that is frequently overlooked. By 1959, two of the seven eastern type-of-farming regions still had less than 100,000 acres of irrigated land. Not only was this figure exceeded by twenty-two California counties in 1954, but in 1959 three counties in California individually irrigated more land than any of the seven eastern water resource regions.

SUMMARY

The changes in agricultural output, inputs, and productivity growth outlined in this chapter reflect sharp modifications in the role of re-

[10] Dalton S. Harrison, *Letter* (Gainesville: University of Florida, Agricultural Extension Service, September 20, 1961).

[11] For an indication of the aggregate effect of variations in rainfall on farm production during this period see J. Stallings, "Weather Indexes," *Journal of Farm Economics,* Vol. 42 (February, 1960), pp. 180–86, and the series of reports by Louis M. Thompson, *An Evaluation of Weather Factors in the Production of Corn, Evaluation of Weather Factors in the Production of Wheat,* and *Evaluation of Weather Factors in the Production of Grain Sorghum* (Ames: Center for Agricultural and Economic Adjustment, Iowa State University, 1962). Thompson's studies indicate that part of the exceptionally rapid yield increases in the late 1950's were due to unusually favorable weather. For an indication of the effect of the farm price variations on the profitability of irrigation see J. E. Kadlec and LaVon Smith, "Will Irrigation Pay?" *Economic and Marketing Information for Indiana Farmers* (Lafayette, Indiana: Purdue University, June, 1961), pp. 1–4.

sources in the growth of agricultural output. Between 1870 and 1900, increased resource inputs represented a major source of agricultural output growth. Between 1900 and 1925, land was an important limiting factor in the slow rate of output growth. Since the mid-1920's, conventional resource inputs have accounted for a progressively smaller share of output growth in American agriculture.

The irrigation, drainage, and soil conservation programs of the last several decades have continued, however, to reflect the concern generated by the effects of resource limitations on agricultural productivity, output, and prices during the early years of the century. Agricultural price programs have also been slow to adjust to the increased productive capacity of American agriculture. As a result, we are confronted with programs which simultaneously attempt to (a) dampen the rate of agricultural output growth by holding productive land out of use, and (b) bring new lands into production through resource development programs.

3

REGIONAL RESOURCE PRODUCTIVITY AND GROWTH MODELS

The historical experience of American agriculture clearly indicates that over periods as long as those typically employed in projections of resource requirements, resource or factor combinations are highly responsive to changes in both factor productivity and factor prices. Furthermore, the combination of farm products utilized by consumers does respond both to changes in tastes and changes in the relative prices of food and fiber products. Resources are drawn into the production of farm products which experience rising product prices relative to the prices of input factors. Also, the effects of expansion or contraction in demand or of changes in comparative advantage in production in one agricultural region are transmitted to other regions.[1]

THE ELASTICITY FRAMEWORK FOR RESOURCE USE PROJECTIONS

The elasticity with which the regional distribution of farm output and factor input combinations respond to economic forces leads to considerable dissatisfaction with the "requirements" framework employed in

[1] For a discussion of recent empirical work in agricultural supply analysis see Marc Nerlove, *The Dynamics of Supply-Estimation of Farmers Response to Price* (Baltimore: The Johns Hopkins Press, 1958). The classic work on interregional supply shifts is R. L. Mighell and J. D. Black, *Interregional Competition in Agriculture* (Cambridge: Harvard University Press, 1954). For two particularly interesting discussions dealing with interregional shifts in resource utilization see G. S. Tolley and L. M. Hartman, "Inter-Area Relations in Agricultural Supply," *Journal of Farm Economics,* Vol. 42 (May, 1960), pp. 453–73; and G. S. Tolley, "Reclamation's Influence on the Rest of Agriculture," *Land Economics,* Vol. 35 (May, 1959), pp. 176–80.

most of the regional resource use projections of the last decade and a half. The typical procedure is to project the regional distribution of production and, then, on the basis of factor-product ratios or trends, to compute the resource inputs required for the output projection.

Use of the "requirements" framework, in its simplest form, involves the implicit assumption that resource combinations and consumption patterns are technologically, institutionally, or psychologically determined and are inelastic with respect to changes in the prices of resource inputs relative to each other, consumption items relative to each other, or resource inputs relative to consumption items.[2]

The requirements framework, if strictly valid, would provide but limited scope for resource policy. The primary function of resource policy would be to assure that society (1) devotes a sufficient share of its savings to resource investment and management activities to permit an acceptable rate of growth in output, and (2) conserves or limits its consumption of resources that have a relatively inelastic output response to increased investment or management.

Resource policy objectives should, however, include efforts to bring about resource input and product combinations which are superior to existing combinations and levels. The role of public policy in achieving this objective includes, in addition to resource investment, research designed to change the rate at which resource inputs can be converted into products and modification of institutions which hold actual conversion rates below desirable levels. The private economy responds to the relative values which society places on the several resource products, and resource combinations and output levels are adjusted to produce higher returns to the resources than they could earn in alternative uses. Product and factor prices play a crucial role in guiding both public and private

[2] For further discussion of the conceptual limitations of the "requirements" framework see S. V. Ciriacy-Wantrup, "Conceptual Problems in Projecting the Demand for Land and Water," in Harold Halcrow (ed.), *Modern Land Policy* (Urbana: University of Illinois, 1961), pp. 42–67; and "Projections of Water requirements in the Economics of Water Policy," *Journal of Farm Economics,* Vol. 43 (May, 1961), pp. 197–214.

For an attempt to introduce the possibilities of nonlinear input substitution empirically see V. W. Ruttan, "The Contribution of Technological Change to Farm Output, 1950–75," *Review of Economics and Statistics,* Vol. 38 (February, 1956), pp. 61–69.

resource investment decisions and in allocating the flow of services from resource investments among competing uses.

The development of an operational "elasticity" approach to regional resource use projections could provide a much more useful framework for the analysis of both public and private resource policy than the requirements approach. Ideally, it should include, for each region, (a) factor supply functions for all resource and other inputs, (b) transportation rates or cost functions for inputs and final products, (c) the geographic location of inputs and markets, (d) production functions relating input levels to output levels for each product, and (e) demand functions for each product.[3] The system should also incorporate changes in the availability of production factors, changes in technology, and changes in consumer tastes over time.

It is easy, of course, to be overly critical of "requirement" approaches and to claim too much for "elasticity" approaches. The requirement approach, particularly in its linear programming or activity analysis form, can be modified to overcome many of the limitations suggested above.[4] The major limitation of these more sophisticated versions of the requirement approach is their almost insatiable appetite for data. As a result, empirical applications of the activity analysis approach in the irrigation and water resource fields have, in the past, largely been confined to a relatively few activities and to limited geographic areas.[5] Empirical studies which have attempted to deal with a complex set of activities for major geographic areas have typically employed what might be termed "aggregate budgeting" rather than the more sophisticated programming techniques.

The "elasticity" approach is limited by an opposite deficiency. Models currently developed typically have not been able to absorb as much data

[3] Leon N. Moses, "Location and the Theory of Production," *Quarterly Journal of Economics,* Vol. 72 (May, 1958), pp. 259–72.

[4] See, for example, Ivan M. Lee, *Optimum Resource Development: A Preliminary Statement of Methodology for Quantitative Analysis* (University of California Agricultural Experiment Station, Giannini Foundation of Agricultural Economics, Mimeographed Report No. 206, July, 1958).

[5] See, for example, G. S. Tolley and V. S. Hastings, "Optimal Water Allocation: The North Platte River," *Quarterly Journal of Economics,* Vol. 74 (May, 1960), pp. 279–95; George A. Pavelis and John F. Timmons, "Programming Small Watershed Development," *Journal of Farm Economics,* Vol. 42 (May, 1960), pp. 225–40.

as many analysts would like to incorporate into their models. Statistical models which include large numbers of variables tend to be limited by lack of statistical significance of the elasticity coefficient; those which include few variables, by biased elasticity coefficients.[6] Decisions with respect to the appropriate framework for analysis must depend, therefore, on both the data with which the analyst has to work and the objectives of the analysis.

Elasticity models of the complexity described above are not operationally feasible at the present time. However, the ones outlined in this chapter incorporate a number of the major features of the ideal approach. A *productivity model* is developed to permit a comparison of current resource productivity and cost levels. Then a *demand model* and an *equilibrium model* are developed to facilitate projection of future farm output and factor input levels. The basic distinction between these two models—both of which build on the relationships utilized in the productivity model—lies in the determination of output growth in each region. In the demand model the regional output levels are determined from outside the system, while in the equilibrium model they are determined simultaneously along with factor input levels.

THE PRODUCTIVITY MODEL

The productivity model consists of three equations: (1) an aggregate regional production function of the Cobb-Douglas (linear in the logarithms) form, and (2) two marginal value product functions for each region. The equations are presented in Table 3.

The production function was estimated statistically from county data by least-squares procedures. The marginal value product functions were obtained by taking the first partial derivative of the production function, first with respect to irrigated land (X_4) and then with respect to current operating expenses (X_6).

The marginal value product of irrigated land can be estimated from equation (2.0) and of current operating expenses from equation (2.1). The marginal value product of irrigated land measures the change in the

[6] Zvi Griliches, "Specification Bias in Estimates of Production Functions," *Journal of Farm Economics,* Vol. 39 (February, 1957), pp. 8–20.

TABLE 3. The Productivity Model

Equations:

A Cobb-Douglas (linear in the logarithms) production function for each region:

(1) $$X_0 = AX_4^{b_4} X_6^{b_6}.$$

A marginal value product function for irrigated land and operating expenses for each region:

(2.0) $$\lambda_4 = (X_0/X_4)b_4 ,$$

(2.1) $$\lambda_6 = (X_0/X_6)b_6 .$$

Notation: The following notation is adopted to be consistent with that used in later sections of the study. See Chapter 4 for a discussion of the alternative production functions estimated in the study.

X_0 – value of farm products sold ($)
X_4 – irrigated land (acres)
X_6 – current operating expenses ($)
λ_4 – marginal value product of irrigated land ($/acre)
λ_6 – marginal value product of operating expenses ($/unit)
A – constant term in the production function
b_4 – productivity coefficient for irrigated land
b_6 – productivity coefficient for operating expenses

value of total output that will result from changing the amount of irrigated land by one acre. The marginal value product of current operating expense measures the variation in the value of total output that will result from varying the use of current operating expense by one unit. If the marginal value product of a particular input exceeds the cost of adding additional units of that input to the production process, net returns can be improved by expanding the use of the particular input. If the marginal value product of a particular input is less than the cost of adding additional units of that input to the production process, net returns can be improved by reducing the use of the particular input. Application of this principle may, of course, require reductions in the use of some inputs, expansion in the use of other inputs, and changes in the level of output in order to achieve an appropriate balance or "equilibrium" among input levels and between input and output levels.

A graphical interpretation of the productivity model is presented in Figure 5. The downward sloping curve represents the short-run derived demand function for irrigated land with regional farm output specified at the level D_{54}. The curve was traced out, using equation (2), by setting the acreage of irrigated land (X_4) at alternative levels and solving for the marginal value productivity of irrigated land (λ_4) consistent with the specified output level (D_{54}).

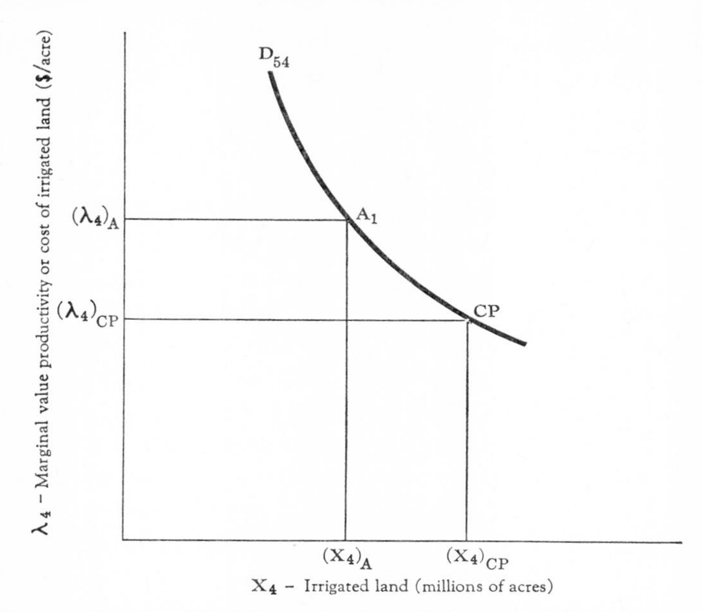

FIGURE 5. Graphical Interpretation of the Productivity Model.

The model can be used to determine whether farmers could more profitably use additional acres of irrigated land, or any other input, to produce the specified output level. Assume, for example, that farmers were using an amount of irrigated land equal to $(X_4)_A$ in 1954 and that current practice[7] capital and operating costs, including the cost of water, were $(\lambda_4)_{CP}$. Since the actual marginal value productivity of irrigated land $(\lambda_4)_A$ is higher than $(\lambda_4)_{CP}$, net returns can be increased by expanding the use of irrigated land to $(X_4)_{CP}$. At this level, the cost per acre would equal the marginal value productivity per acre of irrigated land

[7] The term "current practice costs" is used throughout this study to reflect the actual historical accounting prices or costs incurred by farmers for capital and operating expense inputs. The term "full costs" refers to the estimated prices or costs assuming mid-1950 prices for items purchased from the private sector and no subsidies for items such as irrigation water purchased from the public sector. Current practice costs may be lower than full costs because prices of inputs purchased from the private sector are lower than the mid-1950 prices or because prices or costs of items such as irrigation water purchased from the public sector have been subsidized to reduce the cost to farmers below the full cost level. The computation of current practice and full cost levels is discussed for western water resource regions in Chapter 4.

and, assuming that similar criteria are met for other inputs, net returns to the firm or the region would be maximized.

THE DEMAND MODEL

In the demand model the projected over-all output of farm products is determined from outside the system, as in the requirements approach. Relationships between inputs of irrigated land and other inputs, however, assume a nonlinear form.

The model consists of five relationships and/or identities. These include: (1) a production function of the Cobb-Douglas (linear in the logarithms) form; (2) a derived demand function for irrigated land defined by the first partial derivative of the production function with respect to land at alternative output levels;[8] (3) an identity equating the calculated marginal value productivity of irrigated land to the cost of bringing an acre of irrigated land into production, which serves as a perfectly elastic supply relationship for irrigated land;[9] (4) a national farm output projection based on the anticipated rate of growth of population and per capita income and an estimate of the income elasticity of demand; and (5) a regional output projection based on a dampened trend in the historical relationship between regional and national output growth.

The equations and identities utilized in the demand model are presented in Table 4. In the demand model the level of farm output in any

[8] Edwards has argued that the Cobb-Douglas production function implicitly assumes an elastic demand for all factors and that derived demand functions for factor inputs based on the Cobb-Douglas production function are, therefore, inappropriate if the possibility of an inelastic demand exists. See Clark Edwards, "Demand Elasticity in the Factor Market as Implied by Cobb-Douglas Production Functions," *Journal of Farm Economics,* Vol. 43 (February, 1961), p. 192. More recently Brandow has shown that the Edwards conclusion is valid for an individual firm with a perfectly elastic demand for its products but that it does not hold for an industry or a region unless its demand is also perfectly elastic. See G. E. Brandow, "Demand for Factors and Supply of Output in a Perfectly Competitive Industry," *Journal of Farm Economics,* Vol. 44 (August, 1962), pp. 895–99. Aggregate demand for farm output is highly inelastic at the national level. Although demand at the regional level is less inelastic than at the national level, it is certainly far from perfectly elastic.

[9] In Chapter 5, some of the limitations of the perfectly elastic supply function assumption are modified by raising the cost level and restricting the rate of adjustment toward the equilibrium position.

region, for any specified year, is given by equations (4) and (5). Given the specified level of output in each region and the equation for the production function, the model can be solved to obtain the number of acres of irrigated land in each region which equates the annual marginal value productivity of irrigated land with a specified annual return per acre of irrigated land.

TABLE 4. The Demand Model

Equations and Identities:

A Cobb-Douglas (linear in the logarithms) production function for each region:

(1) $$ {}_R X_{0t} = {}_R A \, {}_R X_{4t}^{R\ b_4} \, {}_R X_{6t}^{R\ b_6}. $$

A derived demand function for irrigated land in each region:

(2) $$ {}_R X_{4t} = ({}_R X_0 / {}_R \lambda_4) {}_R b_4 \, . $$

An identity (equating the calculated marginal value productivity with the budgeted average cost level) serving as a perfectly elastic supply function:

(3) $$ {}_R \lambda_{4t} = {}_R C_4 \, . $$

The national output projection:

(4) $$ {}_N X_{0t} = X_{01} \left(\frac{P_t}{P_1} \right) \left[1 + \left(\frac{Y_t - Y_1}{Y_1} \right)^e \right]. $$

The regional output projections (a dampened trend relative to the national projection):

(5) $$ {}_R X_{0t} / {}_N X_{0t} = ({}_R X_{01} / {}_N X_{0t}) \left[(1 + r) \left(1 + \frac{t-1}{t} r \right) \left(1 + \frac{t-2}{t} r \right) \cdots \left(1 + t - \frac{t+1}{t} r \right) \right]. $$

Notation:
X_0 – value of farm products sold ($)
X_4 – irrigated land (acres)
X_6 – current operating expenses ($)
λ_4 – marginal value product of irrigated land ($ /acre)
C_4 – average annual cost of irrigated land ($ /acre)
t – time, 1···26 (1954–80)
P – population (number)
Y – per capita income ($ /person)
A – constant term in the production function
b_4 – productivity coefficient for irrigated land
b_6 – productivity coefficient for operating expenses
e – income elasticity of demand for farm products
r – rate of change in regional share of national output in past period
N – national total or a variable measured at the national level
R – regional total or a variable measured at the regional level

Interregional equilibrium with respect to irrigated land can be achieved by specifying that the annual rate of return per acre of irrigated land equal the annual costs of bringing an acre of irrigated land into production and producing a crop in each region.

A graphical interpretation of the solution to the demand model is presented in Figure 6. The two downward sloping curves are graphic representations of the derived demand functions with regional farm output specified at the alternative levels D_{54} and D_{80}. The demand curves, D_{54} and D_{80}, were traced out by setting the marginal productivity of irrigated land (λ_4) at alternative levels and solving for the acreage of irrigated land (X_4) consistent with the specified output levels.

The model can be used to explore the effect of both changes in the derived demand for irrigated land and in costs. If, for example, $(\lambda_4)_{FC}$ represents the level at which the marginal value productivity per acre of irrigated land is equated with the sum of the annual costs per acre incurred by public and private agencies (a) in providing storage and distribution facilities, (b) in bringing additional land into production, and (c) in producing a crop, then farmers will maximize net returns by utilizing $(X_4)_{FC}$ acres of irrigated land when the derived demand is at the D_{54} level and $(X_4)_{FC'}$ when the derived demand is at the D_{80} level. If, however, charges for water storage and distribution were set at some lower level such as $(\lambda_4)_{CP}$ by shifting part of irrigation costs to power consumers or taxpayers, for example, farmers could maximize net returns by utilizing $(X_4)_{CP}$ acres of irrigated land when the derived demand is at the D_{54} level and $(X_4)_{CP'}$ acres of irrigated land when the derived demand is at D_{80}.

THE EQUILIBRIUM MODEL

The equilibrium model differs in many respects from either "requirements" projections or "demand" projection models. In essence it indicates the irrigated acreage which would result in a situation characterized by profit maximization, constant input and product prices, and no change in the technology available to irrigators. In the solution of the model, regional output and input levels are determined simultaneously. If a projection indicates a greater irrigated acreage than that which results

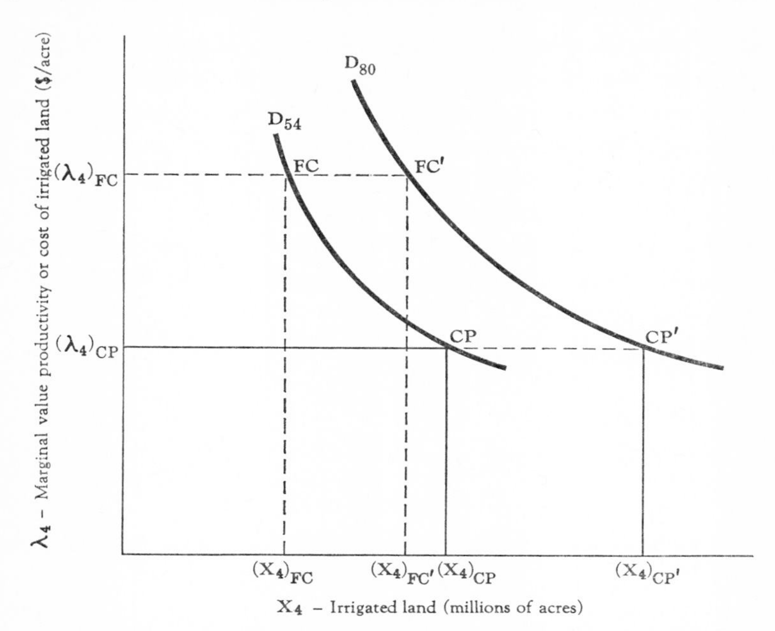

FIGURE 6. Graphical Interpretation of the Demand Model.

from the solution of the equilibrium model, it must imply that relative prices of inputs and outputs or factors affecting productive efficiency have changed. Such assumptions are easily hidden and remain implicit in projection procedures. The solution of the equilibrium model is thus presented not as a projection for a specific future date but as a check on the results of procedures aimed at providing acreage projections for specific dates.

The model consists of three equations and two identities. These include: (1) a Cobb-Douglas (linear in the logarithms) production function for each region; (2) marginal value product functions for irrigated land and operating expenses for each region; and, (3) two identities equating the calculated marginal value productivity levels with budgeted average cost levels, which serve as perfectly elastic supply functions for irrigated land and operating expenses in each region.[10]

[10] As indicated earlier some of the limitations of the perfectly elastic supply function assumption are modified in Chapter 5 by raising the cost level and restricting the rate of adjustment toward the equilibrium position.

In this study the production functions and the marginal value product functions are the same as those used in the productivity model. The simultaneous solution for output and input values is achieved by adding the two identities. Interregional equilibrium can be approximated by specifying that the marginal value productivity levels be equated with capital and operating costs per acre in each region.

The equations used in the equilibrium model are presented in Table 5. The solution of the model is illustrated graphically in Figure 7.[11]

TABLE 5. The Equilibrium Model

Equations and Identities:

A Cobb-Douglas (linear in the logarithms) production function for each region:

(1) $${}_RX_0 = {}_RA_R X_4^{R\,b_4}\,{}_RX_6^{R\,b_6}.$$

A marginal value product function for irrigated land and operating expenses for each region:

(2.0) $${}_R\lambda_4 = ({}_RX_0/{}_RX_4)_Rb_4\,,$$

(2.1) $${}_R\lambda_6 = ({}_RX_0/{}_RX_6)_Rb_6\,.$$

Two identities which equate the calculated marginal value productivity levels with budgeted average cost levels which serve as perfectly elastic supply functions for irrigated land and operating expenses in each region:

(3.0) $${}_R\lambda_4 = {}_RC_4\,,$$

(3.1) $${}_R\lambda_6 = {}_RC_6\,.$$

Notation:

X_0 – value of farm products sold ($)
X_4 – irrigated land (acres)
X_6 – current operating expenses
λ_4 – marginal value product of irrigated land ($/acre)
λ_6 – marginal value product of operating expenses ($/unit)
C_4 – average annual cost of irrigated land ($/acre)
C_6 – equilibrium marginal value product of operating expenses ($/unit)
t – time, 1···26 (1954–80)
A – constant term in the production function
b_4 – productivity coefficient for irrigated land
b_6 – productivity coefficient for operating expenses
R – regional total or a variable measured at the regional level

[11] The following discussion draws heavily on: Glenn L. Johnson, "The Labor Utilization Problem in European and American Agriculture," *Journal of Agricultural Economics,* Vol. 14 (June, 1960), pp. 73–87; Glenn L. Johnson, "The State of Agricultural Supply Analysis," *Journal of Farm Economics,* Vol. 42 (May, 1960), pp. 435–52; Clark Edwards, "Resource Fixity and Farm Organization," *Journal of Farm Economics,* Vol. 41 (November, 1959), pp. 747–60.

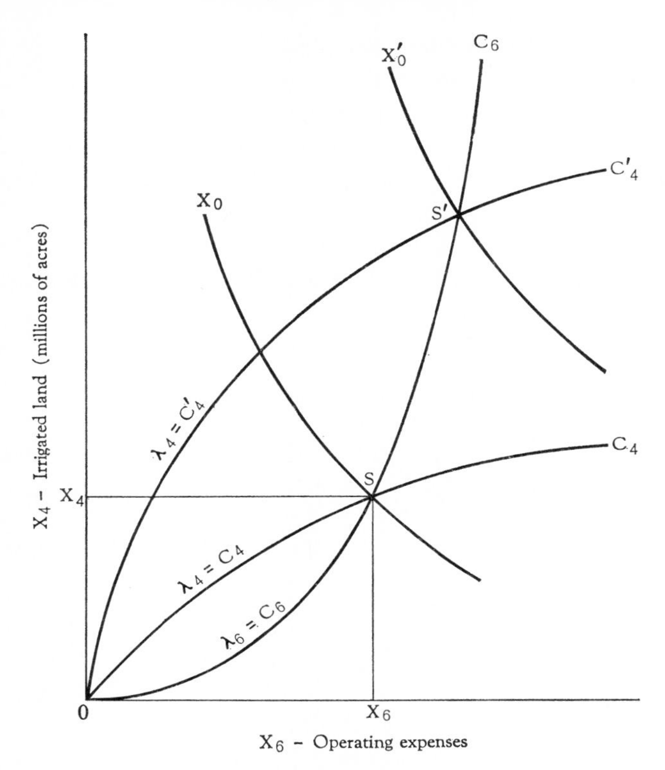

FIGURE 7. Isovalue Product Map for Irrigated Cropland and Operating Expenses.

The line $0C_4$ is the isomarginal value product line for irrigated land (X_4). It is the locus of all points on the value productivity or production surface where the marginal value product of irrigated land (X_4) is equal to the specified cost level (C_4). Any combination of irrigated land, operating expenses, and output described by a point to the left of $0C_4$ would result in a lower marginal value productivity for irrigated land than the level described by $0C_4$. Any combination to the right of $0C_4$ would result in a higher marginal value productivity for irrigated land than the level described by $0C_4$.

The line $0C_6$ is the isomarginal value product line for operating expenses (X_6). It is the locus of all points on the value productivity surface where the marginal value product of operating expenses (X_6) is equal to the specified cost level (C_6). Any combination of irrigated land, operating expenses and output described by a point to the right of $0C_6$ would result in a lower marginal value productivity for operating expense than the level along $0C_6$. Any combination described by a point to the left of $0C_6$ would result in a higher marginal value productivity for operating expense than along $0C_6$.

The line designated X_0 represents one member of the family of isovalue product lines derived from the production function. The isovalue product line is the locus of points describing alternative combinations of irrigated land (X_4) and operating expenses (X_6) which will result in the specified level of output (X_0).

Intersection of X_0, $0C_4$ and $0C_6$ at S represents a graphical interpretation of the solution of the three equations and two identities listed above. The solution at S identifies the optimum level of output (X_0), irrigated land (X_4), and operating expense (X_6), given the shape of the production surface and the "cost" levels for irrigated land (C_4) and operating expense (C_6).

The area bounded by X_4S and X_6S is of particular interest for the analysis of irrigation policy. If output is less than X_0 and the input combination is bounded by $0C_4$ and $0C_6$ in a water resource region, the marginal value productivity of both factors is above the specified cost levels C_4 and C_6. Movement toward the optimum position at S will involve a rise in output, increased use of both factors, and a lower marginal value product for both factors. In the area bounded by OX_4, X_4S and $0C_4$ (below S), the marginal value productivity of irrigated land is lower than C_4 and the marginal value productivity of operating expenses is higher than C_6. Movement toward the optimum at S will involve a rise in output, increased use of both factors, a rise in the marginal value productivity of irrigated land, and decline in the marginal value productivity of operating expenses. In the area bounded by OX_6, X_6S and OC_6 (below S), the marginal value productivity of irrigated land is higher than C_4 and the marginal value productivity of operating expenses is lower than C_6. Movement toward the optimum at S will involve a rise in output, increased use of both factors, a fall in the marginal value productivity of irrigated land and rise in the marginal value productivity of operating expenses.

If the resource combination in a water resource region lies outside the area bounded by X_4S and X_6S, a reduction in the use of one or both factors of production will be necessary if the optimum input combination and output level are to be achieved.

Output expansion is typically easier for the firm to achieve by expanding the utilization of both inputs than by balancing increased use of some inputs by decreases in the use of other inputs, particularly when the surplus has limited alternative uses. Only resource combinations described by a point on or inside the area bounded by X_4S and X_6S can, therefore, be regarded as "rational." At points outside this zone returns can be increased only by reducing the input of at least one of the two resource inputs. Since, however, irrigated acreage, once brought into production, is typically abandoned only when rather substantial losses are absorbed, it is more likely that water charges or land prices will be adjusted downward to some current practice level that will permit the land to remain in production.

The effect of holding irrigation costs to farmers below the total amortization and associated cost level can also be illustrated with Figure 7. Let $0C_4$ represent the isomarginal value product line when the value of the marginal product is equated with full amortization and associated costs. Let $0C'_4$ represent the isomarginal value product line when the value of the marginal product is equated with some lower current practice cost level—for example, when power revenues from Bureau of Reclamation projects are used in part to subsidize water costs to agriculture. When the value of the marginal product is equated with full cost amortization and associated costs, the optimum position on the production surface is at S. When it is equated with the current practice cost level, the optimum position is at S'. The distance between $0S'$ and $0S$ measures the excess demand for irrigated land and associated inputs resulting from holding costs below the full amortization and associated cost level.

It is convenient, and perhaps not too inaccurate, to refer to the position on the production surface identified by S as the *ex ante* or pre-investment social optimum and the position identified by S' as the private optimum.[12] These designations apply prior to construction of the irrigation facilities. Once the capital investment has been made, the use of these terms is consistent with short-run economic efficiency as long as the marginal value product exceeds variable costs including internal opportunity costs, i.e., returns to water in alternative uses. Under such circumstances, S' can be identified as both the *ex post* short-run social optimum and the private optimum provided that the net returns to water in alternative uses do not exceed private returns to irrigated land at S'. The private and social optimum solutions will diverge, however, to the extent that the full social costs of irrigation development exceed the charges that are made by society for the irrigation services it provides to the private sector.

The same analysis could be used to illustrate the effect of a technological change which reduces the cost of irrigation. Assume, for example, that a shift from S to S' resulted from a reduction in costs brought about by the introduction of new pumping equipment. The new equilibrium position at S' would then indicate the response of output and the two inputs to the change in costs, and the distance between $0S'$ and $0S$ would measure the socially optimum increment in irrigated land and operating expenses resulting from the technological change.

ESTIMATION OF THE PRODUCTION FUNCTION

The basic relationship in the elasticity models is the agricultural production function for each region. It was assumed that the aggregate regional production functions for major water resource regions could be

[12] Up to this point care has been taken to avoid identifying the acreage of irrigated land that would equate annual marginal value productivities and annual capital and operating cost flows as the optimal level of irrigation development. Definition of an optimal level of irrigated acreage within the restricted framework of modern welfare economics requires, among other conditions, that marginal value productivities and costs be equated for all factor inputs. The limitations of the data and measurement techniques employed in this and other empirical studies is perhaps an even more important factor precluding any such precise balancing of marginal equalities. In spite of these limitations, however, it is useful to employ certain limited optimality assumptions to explore the nature of the production surface and the impact of factor substitution on factor productivities at alternative output levels. For further discussion of the welfare implications of this model see John V. Krutilla, "Welfare Aspects of Benefit-Cost Analysis," *Journal of Political Economy*, Vol. 59 (June, 1961), pp. 226–35.

adequately described by a Cobb-Douglas type production function, and that the functions could be estimated from county data by ordinary least-squares procedures.[13]

The Cobb-Douglas function has a number of important advantages. It provides immediate elasticities of output with respect to the individual factors of production; it permits decreasing marginal returns to come into evidence without using too many degrees of freedom; and it has demonstrated its empirical usefulness at the firm level in agricultural economics research.

The function also has its limitations. It will exhibit increasing, constant, or decreasing returns to scale but only singly and not in combination; complementarity among inputs is forced as the isoproduct curves become asymptotic to the axes; if the level of any input drops to zero the entire function collapses; marginal productivities estimated at points above or below the geometric mean may be subject to serious bias.

In the context of the present study, the most relevant limitation of the function is that marginal productivities estimated at points above or below the geometric mean may be subject to bias. The effect of this limitation becomes apparent in Chapter 5 where an attempt is made to use the estimated production functions in a solution for the optimum output and factor inputs. The fact that the function does produce nonlinear estimates of the elasticities of output with respect to each input and nonlinear rates of substitution among individual inputs is regarded as outweighing the limitations.

In the empirical implementation of the elasticity model, the county is treated as the basic behavior unit, since individual farm data are not readily available. Although there is a good deal of literature which stresses the limitations of this type of aggregation, there is also a fairly

[13] For a comprehensive discussion of the development and use of production functions see E. O. Heady and J. L. Dillon, *Agricultural Production Functions* (Ames: Iowa State University Press, 1960), Chapters 1–7. See also C. B. Haver, "Economic Interpretation of Production Function Estimates," in E. O. Heady, G. L. Johnson, and L. S. Hardin (eds.), *Resource Productivity, Returns to Scale, and Farm Size* (Ames: Iowa State College Press, 1956), pp. 146–50. For discussion of the use of Cobb-Douglas Production functions in the estimation of aggregate regional production functions and their use in productivity models, see V. W. Ruttan, "The Impact of Irrigation on Farm Output in California," *Hilgardia,* Vol. 31 (July, 1961), pp. 69–111.

strong basis for assuming that aggregate economic behavior can be predicted on the basis of relationships estimated from aggregate data.[14]

It is assumed that a single discoverable production function exists for each major water resource region. Whether this results in serious error in the estimates of the productivity coefficients can not be answered on an *a priori* basis. It will be clear from the analysis in later sections that the assumption is clearly not valid in some regions.

A further limitation of the estimation procedure is that the estimated coefficients may reflect the effects of simultaneous interaction among the product demand, factor supply, and aggregate production function. If this criticism is valid, the least-squares method applied to a single equation—in this case the production function—of the complete system of equations which generated the observed inputs and outputs will result in bias in the estimated production elasticities or coefficients. The fact that inputs, particularly irrigated land, tend to be fixed for the production period indicates that this may not be a critical problem in this study.

THE DEMAND AND EQUILIBRIUM MODELS: ADVANTAGES AND LIMITATIONS

In spite of its advantage when compared with various requirements approaches, the demand model outlined in this chapter has a number of serious limitations. The national farm output projection is essentially a requirement projection based on a dampened trend in historical relationships between national and regional output growth. The demand relationship for irrigated land is a 1980 short-run derived demand relationship that takes the output level as given. The solution does not represent long-run equilibrium input and output levels for the particular cost levels. It is assumed, with output specified by the projection and irrigated acreage specified at a level which will equate marginal value productivity and cost levels, that expansion in the inputs of other factors and technological change will be sufficient to permit the production of the projected level of output with no change in the index of product prices relative to the index of factor prices.

[14] Zvi Griliches and Yehuda Grenfeld, "Is Aggregation Necessarily Bad?" *Review of Economics and Statistics,* Vol. 42 (February, 1960), pp. 1–13.

The equilibrium model overcomes some of the theoretical deficiencies of the demand model, but it has its own deficiencies. It lacks the dynamic property of the demand model, which can be solved by the application of certain limited optimization criteria for a specified date such as 1980. Since the solution to the equilibrium model represents the long-run static equilibrium and is not explicitly associated with a particular date, it is presented not as a projection but as a spelling out of the implications of the relative factor prices and the estimated production function.

The model could, of course, be made dynamic by treating the constant terms of the production function or the cost levels in equations (3.0) and (3.1) as functions of time. If this were done, the equilibrium model would become a projection model, and it would be a more sophisticated and conceptually satisfactory one than the demand model. The empirical analysis in this study is not sufficient to expand the equilibrium model into a dynamic model, although an initial step in this direction is made in the "restricted equilibrium" solutions developed for the western water resource regions in Chapter 5.

The equilibrium model imposes a heavier burden than the demand model on the empirical validity of the estimated coefficients of the production function. A bias in the productivity coefficients for irrigated land which might cause relatively minor distortions in the solution for the demand model can, when combined with additional bias in the coefficient for operating expenses, result in a much larger distortion in the solution for the equilibrium model.

The problems involved in achieving valid statistical estimates of the production functions and the limitations of the elasticity models employed in this study cannot be ignored. In spite of these limitations, the elasticity models do permit the explicit introduction of more inclusive nonlinear optimization processes into regional growth models. These processes typically are treated implicitly or are completely ignored in the traditional requirements models.

4

IRRIGATION PRODUCTIVITY AND COST COMPARISONS

The productivity model outlined in the preceding chapter is utilized here to develop estimates of the marginal value productivity for irrigated land in nine western and seven eastern water resource regions. These estimates are then compared with capital and operating costs in order to assess the profitability under current market conditions of land now under irrigation and to provide insight into the profitability of public and private investment in major irrigation projects under factor and product market conditions similar to those in the mid and late 1950's.

Used in this way the marginal value productivity estimates can provide useful guides for public and private planning. They can aid farmers in deciding whether it is worthwhile to purchase water and bring additional irrigated land into production. They can also be used to evaluate public resource investment. Regardless of what the public agencies charge for the water they supply to farmers, the annual marginal value productivity of the irrigated land should approximate the sum of annual capital and operating charges per acre incurred by public and private agencies in providing storage and distribution facilities, bringing additional land into production and producing a crop.[1]

[1] This is an alternative to the procedure frequently used in evaluating public resource investment where the benefit stream is discounted and compared to investment cost. In this analysis, investment cost is amortized and the annual cost stream compared to annual benefits. No attempt is made here to repeat the exhaustive literature on the issues involved in evaluating public resource investment. For a discussion of these issues see the Inter-Agency Committee on Water Resources, Subcommittee on Evaluation Standards, *Proposed Practices for Economic Analysis of River Basin Projects* (The Green Book), (Washington: May, 1958); S. V. Ciriacy-Wantrup, *Resource Conservation Economics and Policy* (Berkeley: University of California Press, 1952), pp. 230–67; Otto

THE REGIONAL PRODUCTION FUNCTION ESTIMATES

As a first step in the implementation of the productivity model, aggregate regional production functions were estimated statistically for each water resource region from county data by least-squares regression procedures. Farm output in each county was measured by the value of farm products sold. The input variables included labor, irrigated land, nonirrigated land, capital other than land, and current operating expenses.

Since primary attention in this report is focused on the productivity of irrigated land, only the major irrigation counties in each region were used as observations for estimating the statistical production functions. In the West a major irrigation county was defined as one with 1,000 acres or more of irrigated cropland. In the East it was defined as one with 500 acres or more of irrigated land. The western regions are the same as those in the Senate Select Committee report, *Water Resources Activities in the United States*. In the East, however, it was necessary to consolidate several of the regions identified in the Senate report in order to have a sufficient number of observations to provide the degrees of freedom necessary for statistical analysis. The eastern water regions were combined as follows: the Northeast includes (1) New England, (2) Delaware and Hudson Rivers, and (3) Chesapeake Bay; the Great Lakes includes (1) Eastern Great Lakes, and (2) Western Great Lakes; the Corn Belt includes (1) Ohio River, (2) Upper Mississippi River, and (3) Lower Missouri River; the Southeast includes (1) Cumberland River, (2) Tennessee River, and (3) Southeast except Florida; and Florida is identified as a separate water resource region. (See Figure 8.)

Prior to initiation of the study by the Senate Select Committee aggregate regional production functions had been estimated for the thirteen type-of-farming regions shown in Figure 9.[2] Analysis of the functions computed for the type-of-farming regions led to some changes in the

---

Eckstein, *Water-Resource Development* (Cambridge: Harvard University Press, 1958), pp. 19–109, 192–263; J. V. Krutilla and Otto Eckstein, *Multiple Purpose River Development* (Baltimore: The Johns Hopkins Press for Resources for the Future, 1958), pp. 15–75; G. S. Tolley, "Analytical Techniques in Relation to Watershed Development," *Journal of Farm Economics*, Vol. 40 (August, 1958), pp. 653–55; J. S. Bain, "Criteria for Undertaking Water-Resource Development," *American Economic Review*, Vol. 50 (May, 1960), pp. 310–20.

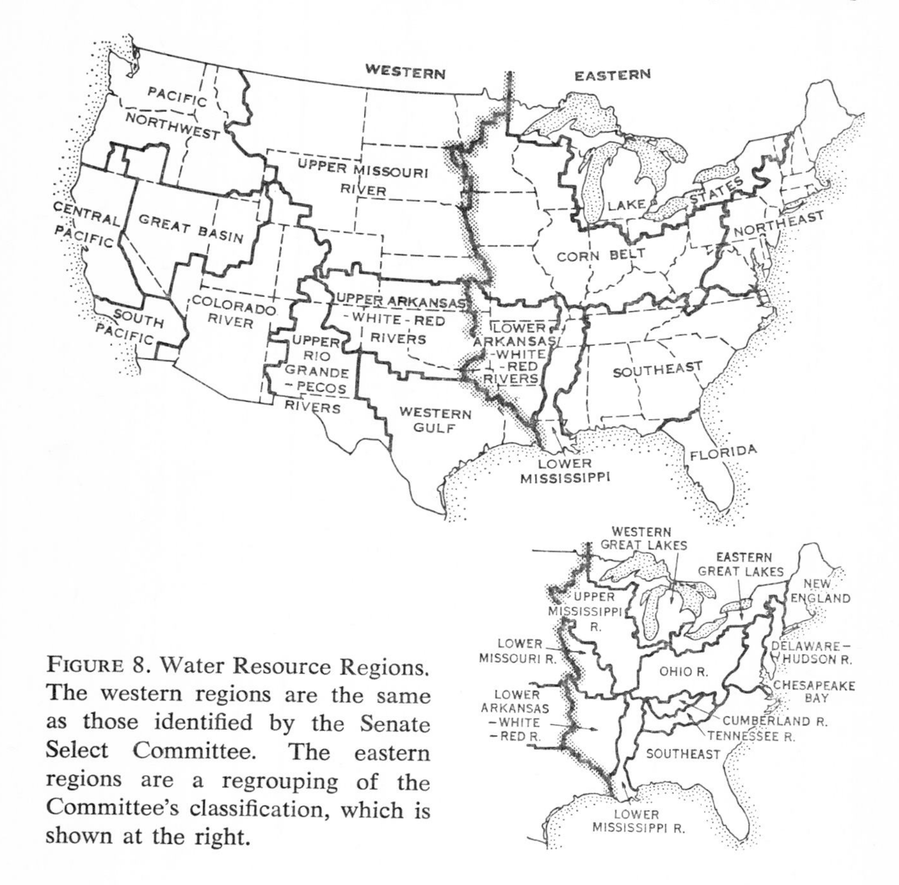

FIGURE 8. Water Resource Regions. The western regions are the same as those identified by the Senate Select Committee. The eastern regions are a regrouping of the Committee's classification, which is shown at the right.

[2] The data for type-of-farming regions are the product of two related studies by J. C. Headley and V. W. Ruttan. Some of the preliminary results of these studies are reported in: J. C. Headley, "The Contribution of Supplemental Irrigation to Agricultural Output in the Eastern United States" (Ph.D. thesis, Purdue University Department of Agricultural Economics, January, 1960); J. C. Headley and V. W. Ruttan, "Regional Differences in the Impact of Irrigation on Farm Output," in *Water Resources and Economic Development of the West,* Report No. 8, Committee on the Economics of Water Resource Development, Western Agricultural Economics Research Council (San Francisco: January, 1960), pp. 107–34 (reprinted in S. C. Smith and E. N. Castle, *Economics and Public Policy in Water Resource Development* (Ames: The Iowa State University Press, 1964); V. W. Ruttan, "The Impact of Irrigation on Farm Output in California," *Hilgardia,* Vol. 31 (July, 1961), pp. 69–111.

variables employed in the analysis based on the water resource regions. A number of alternative production function formulations were also tested for the water resource regions (Table 6). The aggregate production functions that were estimated for each water resource and type-of-farming region are presented in Appendix 1. For most water resource regions at least one, and in some cases all three, of the regional production functions in this appendix provide a satisfactory basis for marginal value productivities estimated for irrigated land and for operating expenses.

There is a tendency in all regions for two of the independent variables —machinery investment (X_2) and livestock investment (X_3)—to exhibit substantial bias as a result of intercorrelation with other independent variables or to fail to meet even fairly liberal criteria for significance. Machinery investment (X_2), in particular, tends to show a high intercorrelation with current operating expense (X_6). It seemed appropriate, therefore, to treat these two variables as complementary in most regions. When machinery investment (X_2) was dropped from the function, the full effect of variations in machinery investment (X_2) and current operating expense (X_6) tended to be reflected in the coefficient for current operating expense (X_6). The livestock investment (X_3)

FIGURE 9. Type-of-Farming Regions.

TABLE 6. Alternative Production Functions Estimated for Type-of-Farming and Water Resource Regions

Factors	Variables used in equations (1) to (5) for type-of-farming regions					Variables used in equations (1) to (7) for water resource regions					
	(1)	(2)	[1](3)	(4)	[2](5)	(1)	(2)	(3)	(4)	[3](6)	[3](7)
Output											
Value of farm products sold ($)	X_0	X_0	X_0	X_0	X_0	X_0	X_0	X_0	X_0	X_0	X_0
Labor											
Total number of family and hired farm workers	X_1	X_1	—	—	—	X_1	X_1	X_1	X_1	X_1	—
Capital other than land											
Machinery and equipment investment ($)	X_2	—	X_2	—	—	X_2	—	—	—	—	—
Livestock investment ($)	—	—	—	—	—	X_3	X_3	—	—	—	—
Irrigated land											
Irrigated cropland harvested (acres)[4]	X_4	X_4	—	X_4	X_4	—	—	—	—	—	—
Irrigated land (acres)[5]	X_4	X_4	X_4	X_4	—	X_4	X_4	X_4	X_4	X_4	X_4
Nonirrigated land											
Nonirrigated cropland harvested (acres)	X_5	X_5	X_5	X_5	—	X_5	X_5	X_5	X_5	—	—
Current operating expenses											
Value of fertilizer, lime, and purchased feed ($)	X_6	X_6	X_6	X_6	X_6	X_6	X_6	X_6	X_6	X_6	X_6

[1] Estimated only for the Northeast, Lake States, and Corn Belt type-of-farming regions.
[2] Estimated only for the California major irrigation counties.
[3] Estimated only for the South Pacific water resource region counties.
[4] Irrigated cropland harvested was used only in western type-of-farming regions.
[5] Includes both harvested cropland and pasture.

Sources: The table and line references cited below refer to U. S. Bureau of the Census, *United States Census of Agriculture* (Washington: Government Printing Office), Vol. I. The 1944 data are from the 1945 Census, the 1949 data are from the 1950 Census, and the 1954 data are from the 1954 Census.

X_0—*Value of all farm products sold,* 1954, table 4, line 3.

X_1—*Number of family and hired workers,* 1954, table 6, line 5.

X_2—*Value of implements and machinery.* Data have not been directly available from the Census of Agriculture since 1944. Estimates for the western regions were constructed by means of a regression equation between the value of implements and machinery and the number of tractors on farms in 1945. From this relationship, 1954 estimates of the value of implements and machinery were obtained by inserting the number of tractors on farms in 1954 and adjusting the resulting estimates by the price indexes shown in the table below. Sources of data used in this estimating procedure were: Value of implements and machinery (in current dollars), 1944, table 1.1, line 44; number of tractors on farms, 1944, table 1.2, line 38, and 1954, table 5, line 64. For the eastern regions the number of tractors on farms was used as an index of machinery investment.

X_3—***Value of livestock investment*** (used in analysis of western regions only). Data on the value of specified classes of livestock on farms are not reported for 1954. An estimate was constructed by use of a regression equation expressing the relationship between the value and the numbers of specified classes of livestock on farms in 1949. From this relationship, 1954 estimates of the value of specified classes of livestock were computed by inserting the livestock numbers reported in 1954 and adjusting the resulting estimates by the price indexes shown in the table below. Sources of the data used in this estimating procedure were as follows: Value of specified classes of livestock on farms, 1949, table 4.1, line 1; number of cattle and calves, 1949, table 4.1, line 16; and 1954, table 7.1, line 3; number of hogs and pigs four months old and older, 1949, table 4.1, line 60; 1954, table 7.1, line 43; number of horses and mules, 1949, table 4.1, line 6, and 1954, table 7.1, line 36; number of sheep and lambs, 1949, table 7.1, line 56, and 1954, table 7.1, line 56; poultry (number of chickens four months old and older plus turkeys kept for breeding), 1949, table 4.2, lines 7 plus 17, and 1954, table 7.2, lines 7 plus 36.

X_4—*Irrigated land.* For western regions, 1954, the sum of irrigated cropland harvested (table 1a, line 25) and irrigated pasture (table 1a, line 29). For eastern regions, 1954, table 1, line 80.

X_5—*Nonirrigated cropland harvested,* 1954, table 1, line 20, minus X_4.

X_6—*Current operating expenses,* 1954, table 6, line 45 (purchased feed) plus line 52 (fertilizer) plus line 57 (lime).

Price Indexes Used in Adjusting 1939 and 1949 Current Dollar Input Values to 1954 Constant Dollar Values

Input item converted to constant dollar value	Price indexes		
	1939	1949	1954
Value of all farm products sold [1]	41.1	97.0	100
Value of all specified crops harvested [1]	38.6	90.1	100
Value of implements and machinery [2]	49.5	86.3	100
Value of specified classes of livestock on farms [2]	47.1	116.6	100
Output-increasing operating expenses: [2]			
1. Fertilizer and lime	65.2	96.8	100
2. Feed	41.2	91.2	100
Equipment operating expenses [2]	63.0	90.1	100

[1] Ivan M. Lee, *Annual Index Numbers of Prices Received, Marketing, and Production. All Farm Commodities and Index Numbers of Acreage of Crops, California, 1910–55,* Giannini Foundation Mimeographed Report No. 201 (Berkeley: University of California, Division of Agricultural Sciences, Agricultural Experiment Station, January, 1958), table 1, col. 1.

[2] U. S. Department of Agriculture, *Agricultural Statistics, 1957* (Washington: U. S. Government Printing Office, 1958), table 681. The value of implements and machinery is from the farm machinery column.

coefficient appears to reflect a significant positive contribution to farm output only in the Colorado River and Great Basin water resource regions. It seems likely that at least part of the reason for lack of significance in the livestock variable (X_3) is due to lack of precision in measuring the capital value of livestock inventories.

THE MARGINAL VALUE PRODUCTIVITY ESTIMATES

Two sets of marginal value productivity estimates are shown in Table 7 for irrigated land, nonirrigated land, and current operating expenses. These were obtained by taking the first partial derivatives of the regional production functions, as indicated in the discussion of the productivity model (Table 3). The first set represents the marginal or incremental contributions to output of unit changes in the resource inputs from the

TABLE 7. Factor Marginal Value Productivity Estimates for Major Irrigation Counties in Western and Eastern Water Resource Regions

Region and equation[1]		Irrigated land		Nonirrigated cropland		Current operating expenses	
		Geometric mean	Arithmetic mean	Geometric mean	Arithmetic mean	Geometric mean	Arithmetic mean
		($/acre)		($/acre)		($/acre)	
Western Water Resource Regions:							
Pacific Northwest	(1)	77.39	63.32	60.93	35.97	2.60	2.12
Central Pacific	(F2)	78.75	91.14	11.02	14.68	3.32	3.14
South Pacific	(7)	413.47	418.16	n.a.	n.a.	1.34	1.10
Colorado River	(2)	11.04	17.13	n	n	4.07	3.82
Great Basin	(3)	29.18	30.84	*	*	2.34	1.97
Upper Rio Grande and Pecos	(1)	81.31	79.12	n	n	3.75	3.82
Western Gulf	(1)	157.46	92.86	23.32	13.74	1.51	.99
Upper Arkansas-White-Red	(1)	86.16	83.58	13.79	11.86	3.21	2.09
Upper Missouri	(2)	76.99	58.87	9.74	6.06	.92	.74
Eastern Water Resource Regions:							
Northeast	(1)	727.31	1,036.82	n	n	1.47	1.35
Great Lakes	(F1)	658.13	1,013.22	22.76	15.85	1.53	1.19
Corn Belt	(F1)	303.75	2,840.75	20.99	20.80	.96	.90
Southeast	(F1)	335.57	806.77	15.96	14.35	2.03	1.78
Florida	(1)	325.23	312.77	38.85	24.58	2.80	2.86
Lower Mississippi	(1)	254.64	169.73	70.41	63.30	*	*
Lower Arkansas-White-Red	(1)	333.11	243.69	*	*	2.13	1.41

n.a. – the variable was not included in the indicated equation.
n – the coefficient was rejected because of negative sign.
* – the coefficient was rejected because it was not significant at the 0.20 level.
[1] Equation numbers refer to the identifying numbers used in Appendix 1. When the equation number is preceded by an "F" it refers to an equation estimated for a type-of-farming region.

1954 geometric mean input and output levels for the major irrigation counties in each water resource region. The second set represents the incremental contributions to output of unit changes in inputs from the 1954 arithmetic mean levels for all counties in each water resource region. (The geometric and arithmetic mean output and resource input levels are presented in Appendix 2.)

Both sets of estimates are important. The ones computed at the geometric mean for the major irrigation counties provide an indication of the productivity of irrigation, and of other major inputs, in the "typical" major irrigation county in each region under 1954 conditions. By comparing these with other productivity estimates derived from studies at the individual farm level in each water resource region it is possible to evaluate critically the "macro" or industry level estimates presented in Table 7 and, indirectly, the validity of the production functions themselves.

The estimates computed at the arithmetic means for all counties in each water resource region provide a measure of "average" rather than "typical" experience. The "average" experience will be employed in the demand and equilibrium models to evaluate the implications of irrigation productivity and cost differences for the expansion of total irrigated acreage in each water resource region. The basis for this procedure is strengthened if the factor productivity levels computed from geometric and arithmetic means show fairly close agreement.

The marginal value productivity of irrigated land tends to be higher in the eastern than in the western water resource regions. And within the eastern regions the marginal value productivity and the average value productivity tend to be highest in the areas where irrigated land has expanded the least. These differences in the value productivity of additional acreage of irrigated land in the two areas reflect, in part, the differential opportunities for expanded production of high value crops.

In the seventeen western states, over 70 per cent of total irrigated acreage is used to produce crops with a relatively low value per acre—food and feed grains and hay and forage (Table 8). Only 15 per cent is used to produce specialty crops with a high value per acre, such as fruits, vegetables, and sugar beets. As new acres of irrigated land have been brought into production, a higher percentage of all irrigated land has been devoted to uses with a lower value per acre. As a result, the incremental contribution or marginal value productivity of irrigated land tends to be lower per acre than the average contribution or average productivity of existing irrigated land.

TABLE 8. Distribution of Irrigated Acreage in Eastern and Western States

(Per cent)

Crop	28 eastern states (1)	17 western states (2)	On Bureau of Reclamation projects (3)
Food and feed grains	25.8	31.0	24.7
Hay and forage	16.2	40.1	43.6
Cotton	8.5	9.4	6.8
Sugar beets	0.1	2.2	5.1
Specialty crops [1]	44.2	13.1	10.2
Other	5.1	4.2	9.6
Total	100.0	100.0	100.0

[1] Includes fruits, vegetables, potatoes, and tobacco.

Source: Data were computed from: (1) U. S. Bureau of the Census, *U. S. Census of Agriculture: 1954*, Vol. III, Special Reports, Part 6, Irrigation in Humid Areas (Washington: U. S. Government Printing Office, 1956), p. 100. (2) U. S. Bureau of Reclamation, *Future Needs for Reclamation in the Western States* (Committee Print No. 14), U. S. Senate Select Committee on National Water Resources (Washington: U. S. Government Printing Office, 1960), p. 3. (3) U. S. Bureau of Reclamation, *Report of the Commissioner of the Bureau of Reclamation, 1959* (Statistical Appendix) (Washington: U. S. Government Printing Office, 1959), pp. 97–98.

In the twenty-eight eastern states, where irrigation is still a relatively minor part of agricultural land use (excepting Florida, Louisiana, and Arkansas), over 44 per cent of total irrigated acreage is used to produce specialty crops with a relatively high value per acre. Until recently, at least, a rather high percentage of additional irrigated acreage was going into such uses. If additional irrigated acreage is brought into production in eastern regions in the near future, however, the low productivity coefficients for irrigated acreage in eastern water resource regions would imply a rather rapid decline in the marginal value productivity of irrigated land in the Northeast, Great Lakes, Corn Belt, and Southeast water resource regions as irrigation is extended to additional acres of the lower productivity crops such as corn, hay, and pasture.

Differences in the product mix provide a partial explanation of the higher marginal productivity estimates in eastern than in western water resource regions and for the rapid decline in marginal value productivity levels in eastern water resource regions as irrigated acreage expands. It also seems apparent that the estimated productivity coefficients for some eastern water resource regions result in overestimates of the marginal value product of irrigated acreage in the East, particularly at the arithmetic mean levels.

In Table 9 comparisons of estimated marginal value productivities and average value of crop production per acre of irrigated land are presented. Although there is a tendency for the marginal value productivity estimates computed at the geometric mean to converge toward the average gross value of crop production per acre levels, the differences remain sufficiently large in the Great Lakes and Lower Arkansas water resource regions to cause considerable doubt about the economic significance of the marginal value productivity levels computed at the geometric mean for these two regions. In the West, the differences between the average and marginal value productivity estimates in the Colorado River water resource region implies limited economic significance for the Colorado River marginal value productivity estimates for irrigated land.

The marginal value productivity estimates for output-increasing current operating expenses (purchased feed, fertilizer, etc.) exhibit fairly wide variations among both eastern and western water resource regions. Studies at the firm level, most of which have been conducted in the eastern regions, have typically shown marginal value productivities per dollar spent falling between $1.25 and $1.75.[3] Ibach and Lindberg have computed substantially higher marginal productivity estimates from aggregate data.[4] Sufficient empirical work is not available on a region

[3] See, for example, E. O. Heady and J. L. Dillon, *Agricultural Production Functions* (Ames: The Iowa State University Press, 1961), p. 556; Irving Hoch, "Estimation of Agricultural Resource Productivities Combining Time Series and Cross Section Data" (Ph.D. dissertation, Department of Economics, University of Chicago, March, 1957), p. 56; Clark Edwards, "Estimation of Farm Resource Productivities from Central Indiana Account Records" (Master's thesis, Department of Agricultural Economics, Purdue University, 1956).

[4] D. B. Ibach and R. C. Lindberg, *The Economic Position of Fertilizer Use in the United States,* Information Bulletin No. 202, U.S. Department of Agriculture (Washington, 1958), p. 7. "The last dollar spent for fertilizer at the 1954 average rates of application on all crops and pasture returned $2.93. The comparable marginal return was $3.40 for intertilled crops and $1.96 for close growing crops and hay and pasture."

TABLE 9. Comparisons of Estimated Marginal Value Productivities and Average Value of Crop Production per Acre of Irrigated Land

($/irrigated acre)

Region	Marginal value productivity per acre of irrigated land		Average gross value of crop production per acre of irrigated land, 1954
	Geometric mean	Arithmetic mean	
Western Water Resource Regions:			
Pacific Northwest	77	63	138
Central Pacific	78	91	201
South Pacific	413	418	416
Colorado River	11	17	166
Great Basin	29	31	58
Upper Rio Grande and Pecos	81	79	156
Western Gulf	157	93	141
Upper Arkansas-White-Red	86	84	96
Upper Missouri	77	59	64
Eastern Water Resource Regions:			
Northeast	727	1,037	
New England			795
Delaware-Hudson			597
Chesapeake Bay			412
Great Lakes	658	1,013	
Eastern Great Lakes			483
Western Great Lakes			420
Corn Belt	304	2,841	
Ohio			293
Upper Mississippi			359
Lower Missouri			68
Southeast	336	807	
Southeast			[1] 473
Cumberland			243
Tennessee			274
Florida	325	313	
Lower Mississippi	255	170	182
Lower Arkansas-White-Red	333	244	81

[1] Including Florida.

Source: Columns 1 and 2 from Table 7. Column 3 from U. S. Department of Agriculture, *Land and Water Potentials and Future Requirements for Water*, Committee Print No. 12, Select Committee on National Water Resources, U. S. Senate, 86th Congress, 1st Session (Washington: U. S. Government Printing Office, 1960), p. 36 (Table 13).

by region basis to check the consistency of each regional estimate with individual farm estimates for the same region. It is clear, however, that for most regions except the Upper Missouri and the Corn Belt the marginal value productivity estimates for operating expenses computed using the productivity coefficients from the regional production functions fall within the range of estimates obtained in other studies.

COST AND PRODUCTIVITY COMPARISONS FOR WESTERN WATER RESOURCE REGIONS

The next step in the analysis is to compare the marginal value productivity estimates presented in Table 7 with capital and operating costs per acre. In these comparisons an attempt will be made to answer two questions that are particularly relevant for public and private irrigation development policy. *First,* how does the marginal productivity of irrigated land compare with current annual water charges and associated costs? This comparison provides insight into the profitability of past irrigation development to farmers under current factor and product market conditions. *Second,* how does the marginal productivity of irrigated land compare with the amortization and associated costs for new irrigation projects currently being considered by federal and other agencies? This comparison of the total amortization and associated costs on potential new projects with current productivity levels on existing irrigated land in each region provides insight into the relative profitability of public and private investment in major irrigation projects under factor and product market conditions similar to those in the mid and late 1950's.[5]

The cost data relevant to the first comparison are presented in Table 10. The data on cost of water to farms reflects the payments made by farmers to the irrigation districts or other water supply enterprises. Where farmers supply their own water a calculation of equivalent costs is made. The data on associated costs include land charges (for acquisition,[6] preparation, maintenance, and taxes), irrigation structures and equipment charges, and other cost items not explicitly included in the production functions estimated for the several water resource regions. They do

[5] Although farm product prices during the mid-1950's were probably somewhat above equilibrium levels, they were apparently closer to equilibrium levels than at any time since the mid-1920's. See V. W. Ruttan and T. T. Stout, "Regional Differences in Factor Shares in American Agriculture: 1925–57," *Journal of Farm Economics,* Vol. 42 (February, 1960), pp. 52–68. For a discussion of equilibrium prices in 1980, see Chapter 6.

[6] Based on dry cropland values on the assumption that this represents the opportunity cost for irrigated cropland.

TABLE 10. Average Current Water and Other Associated Costs[1] to Irrigators Per Acre of Irrigated Land, Western Water Resource Regions

($/acre)

Region	Full cost of water to farms [2]	Associated irrigation costs [3]	Total current irrigation costs
Pacific Northwest	3.36 [a]	40.90	44.26
Central Pacific	8.82 [b]	58.40	67.22
South Pacific	18.41 [c]	97.70	116.11
Colorado River	7.09 [d]	37.50	44.59
Great Basin	2.02 [e]	18.40	20.42
Upper Rio Grande and Pecos	2.85 [f]	37.50	40.35
Upper Missouri	1.99 [g]	22.90	24.89
Upper Arkansas-White-Red	2.52 [h]	[4] 26.34	[4] 28.86
Western Gulf	7.82 [i]	45.20	53.02

[1] Exclusive of labor, fertilizer, or purchased feed. These estimates are computed with the objective of comparison with marginal productivity estimates for irrigated land computed from an equation in which labor and current operating expenses are held constant at the mean.

[2] From U.S. Bureau of the Census, *U.S. Census of Agriculture: 1950, Vol. III, Irrigation of Agricultural Lands* (Washington: U.S. Government Printing Office, 1952), Summary Table 55, p. 88. Full costs are for the areas listed below:
[a] North Pacific
[b] Central Valley, total
[c] Santa Maria River and Basins, South
[d] Gulf of California, total
[e] Great Basin, total
[f] Rio Grande above Fort Quitman, Texas
[g] Missouri River, total
[h] Arkansas River
[i] Rio Grande below Fort Quitman, Texas

[3] Based on cost data assembled by Karl Gertel to estimate the maximum repayment capacities reported in Karl Gertel and Nathaniel Wollman, "Price and Assessment Guides to Western Water Allocation," *Journal of Farm Economics*, Vol. 42 (December, 1960), p. 1336 (Table 2). Associated costs include land charges (for acquisition, maintenance, and preparation), taxes, irrigation structures and equipment charges, and production costs not explicitly included in the variables used in the production functions estimated for the several water resource regions.

[4] Estimated from data for the Upper Missouri and Western Gulf.

not include labor or current operating expenses that are not directly connected with operation and maintenance of the irrigation system; these costs are incorporated separately in the production functions.

The cost data relevant to the comparison of mid-1950 productivity levels with projected amortization and associated irrigation costs on potential federal and other projects are presented in Table 11. These differ in two respects from the data on average current costs. The full cost of water to farms is replaced by (a) the estimated annual amortization cost per equivalent acre, plus (b) a charge for operation and maintenance of irrigation facilities. The estimated annual amortization cost was obtained by computing the annual carrying charges on that portion of total project costs allocated to irrigation. This calculation approximates, therefore, what the farmers who use irrigation water would have to pay if they were charged a rate sufficient to amortize, at a 5.5 per cent interest rate, the investment made by the suppliers of irrigation water.[7] The operation and maintenance costs reported in the Census have been arbitrarily adjusted upward by 50 per cent to reflect cost levels more characteristic of the late 1950's or early 1960's. The other associated irrigation costs are the same in Table 11 as in Table 10.

[7] The appropriate interest rate for use in amortizing investment costs on public investment has received a good deal of attention. According to the Subcommittee on Evaluation Standards of the Federal Inter-Agency River Basin Committee in *Proposed Practices for Economic Analysis of River Basin Projects* (Washington: U.S. Government Printing Office, May, 1958), p. 24, ". . . the average yield on long-term Federal bonds (preferably rounded to nearest ¼ percent) over a sufficiently long period of time to average out the influence of cyclical fluctuations might be uniformly used by all agencies as an approximation of the expected long-term, essentially risk-free rate." In *Water-Resource Development, op. cit.*, pp. 101 and 104, Otto Eckstein suggests that *"the government use a relatively low interest rate for the design and evaluation of projects, but let projects be considered justified only if the benefit-cost ratio is well in excess of 1.0* . . . a combination of interest rates and minimum benefit-cost ratios should be selected which will correspond to a rate of return of 6 percent for a project of average capital intensity. . . . An interest rate of 3 percent and a benefit cost ratio of 1.3 or an interest rate of 2½ percent coupled with a ratio of 1.4 are combinations which will produce an average rate of return . . . of about 6 percent . . ." In *Multiple Purpose River Development, op. cit.*, p. 120, the social cost of capital is estimated to be approximately 5.5 per cent. "Combining all reasonable assumptions that would raise the rate yields an estimate of 7 per cent; conversely, all plausible assumptions that would produce a low rate yield an estimate of 5 per cent. It is our conclusion that the probable value for the economic conditions postulated lies between 5 and 6 per cent." Even higher discounting rates are recommended in Jack Hirshleifer, J. C. DeHaven, and J. W. Milliman, *Water Supply: Economics, Technology and Policy* (Chicago: University of Chicago Press, 1960), pp. 147–48, ". . . the market provides two bench marks which can be used as a guide for practical procedure. The first is the pure rate of interest for long-term investments, which we believe to be currently just above 4 per cent. This rate is to be used in discounting if in fact the estimated stream of costs and benefits can be regarded as certainty-equivalents. . . . .The other bench mark is the opportunity rate of close to 10 per cent implicit in the markets' evaluation of the riskiness of investments of privately owned taxed public utilities. . . . Actually, we believe it fair to state that experience shows the real riskiness of projects engaged in by government agencies to be substantially greater than those in the private sphere, a rate higher than 10 per cent thus being indicated." For an evaluation of the alternative concepts which underlie the selection of an interest rate for evaluation of public investment see Stephen A. Marglin, "The Social Rate of Discount and the Optimal Rate of Investment," *Quarterly Journal of Economics*, Vol. 77 (February, 1963), pp. 95–111.

TABLE 11. Projected Amortization and Associated Irrigation Costs on Potential Projects in Western Water Resource Regions

($/acre)

Water resource region	Projected irrigation investment cost per equivalent acre [1]	Projected annual amortization cost per equivalent acre [2]	Associated costs per acre: Operation and maintenance of irrigation facilities [3]	Associated costs per acre: Other associated irrigation costs [4]	Full amortization and associated costs per acre
Federal Projects					
Pacific Northwest	646	35.53	4.13	40.90	80.56
Central Pacific	681	37.46	12.65	58.40	108.51
South Pacific	2,780	152.90	24.98	97.70	275.58
Colorado River	1,374	75.57	9.02	37.50	122.09
Great Basin	906	49.83	2.64	18.40	70.87
Upper Rio Grande and Pecos	750	41.25	3.66	37.50	82.41
Upper Missouri	1,160	63.80	2.39	22.90	89.09
Upper Arkansas-White-Red	1,167	64.19	3.45	[5] 26.34	93.98
Western Gulf	730	40.15	9.63	45.20	94.98
Other Projects					
Pacific Northwest	484	26.62	4.13	40.90	71.65
Central Pacific	384	21.12	12.65	58.40	92.17
South Pacific	425	23.38	24.98	97.70	146.06
Colorado River	140	7.70	9.02	37.50	54.22
Great Basin	251	13.80	2.64	18.40	34.84
Upper Rio Grande and Pecos	n.a.	n.a.	3.66	37.50	—
Upper Missouri	200	11.00	2.39	22.90	36.29
Upper Arkansas-White-Red	207	11.39	3.45	[5] 26.34	41.18
Western Gulf	659	36.25	9.63	45.20	91.08

n.a. – not available.

[1] Bureau of Reclamation, U.S. Department of the Interior, *Future Needs for Reclamation in the Western States* (Committee Print No. 14), U.S. Senate Select Committee on National Water Resources, 86th Congress, 2nd Session (Washington: U.S. Government Printing Office, 1960), Table 11.

[2] Computed from irrigation cost per equivalent acre assuming an interest rate of 5.5 per cent per year. For justification of this assumption, see J. V. Krutilla and Otto Eckstein, *Multiple Purpose River Development* (Baltimore: The Johns Hopkins Press, for Resources for the Future, 1958), pp. 78–103.

[3] Operation and maintenance costs only. See footnote 2, Table 10, for source. The reported data were adjusted upward by 50 per cent to more closely approximate anticipated cost in the early 1960's.

[4] See footnote 3, Table 10.

[5] Estimated from data for the Upper Missouri and Western Gulf.

In the case of both federal and other projects there is a substantial difference between the current cost of water to farms and the projected annual amortization cost per equivalent acre. The lower current costs reflect, in part, the fact that development costs have been lower on single farm irrigation enterprises and on past projects than on the projects planned for the future. They also reflect, in the case of water supplied by federal projects, the lower interest rates charged by the federal agencies, and the effect of the basin account device.[8]

The two sets of irrigation cost estimates are shown in Table 12 with productivity estimates for each western water resource region. The comparisons indicate that the estimated marginal value productivity exceeds estimated current annual water charges and associated costs in all but one of the nine regions. It falls below current practice cost levels only in

TABLE 12. Comparison of Irrigation Cost and Productivity Estimates for Western Water Resource Regions

($/acre)

Region	Estimated current annual water charges and associated costs [1]	Projected full amortization and associated costs on potential federal projects [2]	Marginal productivity of irrigated land at: Geometric mean [3]	Arithmetic mean [3]
Pacific Northwest	44.26	80.56	77.39	63.32
Central Pacific	67.22	108.51	78.85	91.14
South Pacific	116.11	275.58	413.47	418.16
Colorado River	44.59	122.09	11.04	17.13
Great Basin	20.42	70.87	29.18	30.84
Upper Rio Grande and Pecos	40.35	82.41	81.31	79.12
Western Gulf	53.02	94.98	157.46	92.86
Upper Arkansas-White-Red	28.86	93.98	86.16	83.58
Upper Missouri	24.89	89.09	76.99	58.87

[1] From Table 10.
[2] From Table 11.
[3] From Table 7.

[8] For a more detailed discussion of the procedures used to reduce the repayment burden of irrigators below the level that would amortize public investments in irrigation development, see Otto Eckstein, *Water-Resource Development*, *op. cit.*, pp. 226–36. Also E. F. Renshaw, *Toward Responsible Government* (Chicago: Idyia Press, 1957), pp. 97–103, 113–17, 159–69.

the Colorado River region where, as indicated earlier, the estimate may be particularly poor. In the other eight regions there would be substantial incentive for farmers to expand irrigated acreage if costs to farmers are maintained at or near the current practice levels of the mid-1950's.

In the South Pacific and Western Gulf regions, the marginal productivity of irrigated land in the typical irrigation county (evaluated at the geometric mean) exceeds even the higher projected full amortization and associated costs on potential federal projects. In those two areas continued expansion of irrigation even at relatively high cost would appear to be justified as long as additional quantities of water can be provided at or near the estimated full cost levels.

In two other regions—the Pacific Northwest and the Upper Rio Grande and Pecos—the estimate of amortization and associated costs on potential federal projects exceeds the marginal productivity of irrigated land in the typical irrigation county by less than $5.00. This suggests that irrigation development would be profitable in some parts of these regions even at the relatively high full cost levels projected for federal projects, assuming, of course, that sufficient water is available to satisfy higher-value alternative uses.

There are three other regions—the Central Pacific, Upper Arkansas-White-Red Rivers and Upper Missouri River—where the projected amortization and associated costs on potential federal projects are $5–$20 higher than marginal value productivity of irrigated land in the typical irrigation county. This would seem to imply that in only a limited number of areas within these regions would irrigation development be profitable at the relatively high full cost levels projected for federal projects. The marginal productivity estimates for irrigated land in these areas do, however, approximate or exceed average costs on projected nonfederal projects.

In the two other western water resource regions—the Colorado River and Great Basin—the projected full costs on both federal and other projects exceed the marginal value productivity estimates by a substantial margin. There would appear to be severely restricted opportunities for profitable irrigation development in these two regions if farmers were to bear the full costs that can be reasonably assigned to irrigation.

COST AND PRODUCTIVITY COMPARISONS FOR EASTERN WATER RESOURCE REGIONS

In most eastern regions the expansion of irrigated acreage is limited more by the demand for the higher-value crops grown on irrigated land than by the physical limitations of soil and water availability.[9] Furthermore, irrigation development in the East is primarily a single-enterprise activity. Unless this situation changes it seems reasonable to assume that any change in irrigation costs will result primarily from changes in the price of land and other costs associated with irrigation rather than from higher project development costs as in the West. For eastern regions, therefore, only one question is investigated: How does the marginal productivity of irrigated land compare with the cost of irrigation?

The irrigation cost estimates for the East are made up of two major components: (a) opportunity cost for land, which is measured by the marginal value productivity of nonirrigated cropland in the same region; and (b) other associated costs, which include irrigation equipment costs (interest, depreciation, taxes, insurance, and repairs) and other cost items directly associated with irrigation and not explicitly included in the production function. As in the case of the western water resource regions, the associated costs do not include labor or current operating expenses that are not directly connected with operation and maintenance of the irrigation system.

If irrigation is to be profitable to a farmer, the marginal productivity of the irrigated land must exceed the marginal productivity of the nonirrigated cropland by more than any additional costs associated with the irrigation and not explicitly included in the production function. Comparison of the cost and productivity estimates in Table 13 indicates that, on the basis of 1954 conditions, there is substantial incentive for expansion of irrigated acreage in each of the eastern water regions. Even a substantial discounting for the apparent overestimation of the productivity of irrigated acreage at the geometric mean in the Great Lakes and Lower Mississippi water regions does not alter this conclusion.

[9] J. C. Headley, "Factors Associated with the Location of Supplemental Irrigation in the Humid Area," *Land Economics*, Vol. 37 (May, 1961).

TABLE 13. Comparisons of Irrigation Cost and Productivity Estimates for Eastern Water Resource Regions

($/acre)

Region	Irrigation cost			Marginal productivity of irrigated land at	
	Opportunity cost for land [1]	Other associated costs [2]	Total	Geometric mean	Arithmetic mean
Northeast	10	49	59	727.31	1,036.82
Great Lakes	23	49	62	658.13	1,013.22
Corn Belt	21	49	70	303.75	2,840.75
Southeast	16	49	65	335.57	806.77
Florida	39	41	80	325.57	312.77
Lower Mississippi	70	41	111	254.64	169.73
Lower Arkansas-White-Red	7	41	48	333.11	243.67

[1] The estimates presented for all regions except the Northeast and the Lower Arkansas-White-Red are based on the marginal productivity estimates at the geometric mean for nonirrigated cropland in major irrigation counties presented in Table 7. The estimates for the Lower Arkansas-White-Red are computed from the coefficient in equation (3). Since no reliable productivity coefficient for nonirrigated cropland is available for the Northeast, the estimate was computed by multiplying the estimated 1959 average plowland value per acre by an interest rate of 5.5 per cent.

[2] Based on an unpublished budget assembled by W. S. Eichberger and Karl Gertel of the Land and Water Research Branch, U.S.D.A. The associated cost estimates for Florida, the Lower Arkansas, and the Lower Mississippi river basins are based on an assumed irrigated acreage per farm of 57 acres. In other areas the cost estimates are based on an assumption of 32 acres per farm. Associated costs are estimated exclusive of labor and output-increasing current operating expenses.

PROSPECTS FOR EXPANSION OF IRRIGATED ACREAGE

The productivity and cost comparisons put comparatively little strain on the data or the analysis and are in many respects the most dependable indicators of future change presented in this book. A positive differential between irrigation productivity and cost indicates the existence of economic pressure for expansion of irrigated acreage, and a negative differential indicates incentives for contraction.

At product price and cost levels near those that prevailed in the middle or late 1950's, the expansion of irrigated acreage can be expected to continue in both eastern and western water resource regions. If, however, water and associated charges on public projects in the West are raised to reflect full amortization costs instead of being held at current practice cost levels or if farm product prices drop sharply below mid-1950 levels, the expansion would be sharply curtailed in most western regions.

5

IRRIGATED ACREAGE PROJECTIONS TO 1980

The resource productivity and cost comparisons provide useful guides to the direction of future changes, but they do not project the extent of the expansion or the contraction that might be expected. In this chapter a projection of irrigated acreage is developed for each water resource region, based on a solution of the demand model for each region. These projections, as well as the figures derived from the solution of the equilibrium model, are shown in Table 14 for the West and Table 16 for the East. They are then compared in Table 17 with the projections prepared for the Senate Select Committee on National Water Resources by the Department of Agriculture and by the Bureau of Reclamation.

IRRIGATED ACREAGE PROJECTIONS FOR WESTERN WATER RESOURCE REGIONS

Demand Model Projections

The demand model projections are constructed by extending the productivity model to include two equations which relate regional output growth to national output growth and an identity which equates the calculated marginal value productivity of irrigated land to the capital and operating costs per acre of irrigated land (see Tables 3 and 4). Solutions are presented in Table 14 with the marginal value productivity of irrigated land equated to both current practice and full cost levels. Demand model solutions are presented for 1954 as well as 1980. This permits a comparison of the acreage of irrigated land reported in the

TABLE 14. Alternative Demand and Equilibrium Model Projections of Farm Output and Irrigated Acreage for Western Water Resource Regions

Region	Reported and estimated		1954 Demand model solutions		1980 Demand model solutions		1980 Equilibrium solutions		
	1954	1959	Current practice cost	Full cost	Current practice cost	Full cost	Current practice cost	Full cost	Re-stricted
	(1)	(2)	(3)	(4)	(5)	(6)	(7)	(8)	(9)
Pacific Northwest									
Output (million $)	1,173		1,173	1,173	2,004	2,004	1,758	1,300	1,358
Irrigated land (thousand acres)	4,353	4,807	6,228	3,421	10,637	5,844	9,328	3,789	4,326
Productivity of									
Irrigated land ($/acre)	63.32		44.26	80.56	44.26	80.56	44.26	80.56	74.76
Operating expenses ($/$)	2.12						1.50	1.50	1.50
Central Pacific									
Output (million $)	1,586		1,586	1,586	3,403	3,403	14,378	6,228	5,320
Irrigated land (thousand acres)	6,064	6,300	8,222	5,093	17,640	10,928	74,541	20,002	14,581
Productivity of									
Irrigated land ($/acre)	91.14		67.22	108.51	67.22	108.51	67.22	108.51	127.24
Operating expenses ($/$)	3.14						1.50	1.50	1.50
South Pacific									
Output (million $)	579		579	579	1,092	1,092	71,924	2,184	812
Irrigated land (thousand acres)	789	737	2,843	1,198	5,358	2,257	352,962	4,516	1,311
Productivity of									
Irrigated land ($/acre)	418.16		116.11	275.58	116.11	275.58	116.11	275.58	352.03
Operating expenses ($/$)	1.15						1.50	1.50	1.50
Colorado River									
Output (million $)	534		534	534	1,169	1,169	958	846	1,032
Irrigated land (thousand acres)	2,813	3,025	1,083	395	4,584	1,674	1,364	440	2,723
Productivity of									
Irrigated land ($/acre)	17.13		44.39	122.09	44.39	122.09	44.39	122.09	24.07
Operating expenses ($/$)	3.82						1.50	1.50	1.50
Great Basin									
Output (million $)	170		170	170	248	248	370	89	180
Irrigated land (thousand acres)	1,936	1,830	2,924	843	4,264	1,229	6,346	439	1,647
Productivity of									
Irrigated land ($/acre)	30.85		20.42	70.87	20.42	70.87	20.42	70.87	38.29
Operating expenses ($/$)	1.97						1.50	1.50	1.50

TABLE 14—Continued.

	(1)	(2)	(3)	(4)	(5)	(6)	(7)	(8)	(9)
Upper Rio Grande and Pecos									
Output (million $)	233		233	233	418	418	[1] 418	[1] 418	[1] 418
Irrigated land (thousand acres)	1,132	1,247	2,220	1,087	3,992	1,955	[1] 1,559	[1] 1,559	[1] 1,559
Productivity of									
Irrigated land ($/acre)	79.12		40.35	82.41	40.35	82.41			
Operating expenses ($/$)	3.82								
Western Gulf									
Output (million $)	1,407		1,407	1,407	2,317	2,317	1,682	1,235	1,289
Irrigated land (thousand acres)	4,432	4,785	7,761	4,333	12,785	7,137	9,283	3,805	4,306
Productivity of									
Irrigated land ($/acre)	92.86		53.02	94.98	53.02	94.98	53.02	94.98	87.59
Operating expenses ($/$)	.99						1.50	1.50	1.50
Upper Arkansas-White-Red									
Output (million $)	948		948	948	1,289	1,285	1,416	1,097	1,175
Irrigated land (thousand acres)	1,407	2,388	4,082	1,254	5,530	1,698	6,144	1,462	2,149
Productivity of									
Irrigated land ($/acre)	83.54		26.86	93.98	26.86	93.98	28.86	93.98	68.45
Operating expenses ($/$)	2.09						1.50	1.50	1.50
Upper Missouri									
Output (million $)	2,964		2,964	2,964	4,528	4,528	3,002	2,598	2,791
Irrigated land (thousand acres)	4,622	6,029	10,938	3,056	16,708	4,668	11,083	2,680	5,426
Productivity of									
Irrigated land ($/acre)	58.90		24.89	89.09	24.89	89.09	24.89	89.09	47.28
Operating expenses ($/$)	.74						1.50	1.50	1.50
Total (all western regions) [2]									
Output (million $)	9,595		9,595	9,595	16,468	16,463	95,906	15,995	14,375
Irrigated land (thousand acres)	27,550	31,148	46,301	20,680	81,497	37,390	472,610	38,692	38,028

[1] The total cost demand model projections is accepted as the best projection for output for the Upper Rio Grande and Pecos. The irrigated acreage figure shown is the U.S.D.A. projection. See text discussion.

[2] Totals computed before rounding.

Sources: Output and irrigated acreage in column (1) were tabulated from sources identified in Table 6. Productivity alternates were calculated as indicated in discussion of the productivity model in Chapters 3 and 4. The column (2) figures are tabulations from 1959 Census of Agriculture and Irrigation, supplied by Land and Water Branch, RDED, ERS, U.S. Department of Agriculture.

Census of Agriculture with the acreage that would have equated marginal value productivity to current practice and to full cost levels at the 1954 level of farm output in each region.

The national output projection for 1980 assumes a population of 260 million at that time, a 40 per cent rise in per capita income between 1954 and 1980, and an income elasticity of demand of 0.15. It also assumes that the prices of farm products will bear approximately the same relationship to prices paid by farmers as in the mid-1950's when the parity ratio stood at about 80. The regional output projections are based on an assumption that the annual rate of change in each region's share of national farm output between 1929 and 1954 will decline linearly to zero by 1980. This is, in effect, an assumption that the forces which brought about regional shifts in farm output between 1929 and 1954 will gradually "play out" by 1980.[1]

Solution of the demand model with capital and operating costs held at current practice levels resulted in a projected irrigated acreage in 1980 above the 1954 and 1959 levels in each western water resource region (see Table 14). If irrigated land is made available and pricing policies are adopted which permit farmers to equate the marginal value productivity of irrigated land with current practice costs, the demand model solution projects a more than doubling of irrigated acreage in the entire region between 1959 and 1980.

The results are considerably different when capital charges and associated costs on irrigated land are permitted to rise to the full cost level indicated for federal projects. A rise in irrigated acreage is then projected

[1] This assumption is clearly a major weakness of the dampened trend procedure. The forces which brought about the changes in the regional distribution of farm output between 1929 and 1954 can be expected to become dampened over the next several decades. It seems fairly certain, however, that other technological, economic, and institutional forces will come into existence to replace the forces that are now playing out. To the extent that these forces seriously reinforce or reverse present tendencies the projections of the regional distribution of farm output based on the dampened trends will be in error. The dampened trend procedure does, however, seem superior to any of the other mechanical methods commonly used to distribute national output growth among regions. It would appear to be clearly superior, for example, to either an assumption that each region will account for the same share of national farm output in 1980 as in some recent period or that the share of national farm output in each region will continue to rise or decline at the same rate as during some past period. For further discussion of both national and regional farm output projections see Appendix 3.

in only five of the nine western water resource regions: the three Pacific water resource regions—Pacific Northwest, Central Pacific, and South Pacific—plus the Western Gulf and the Upper Rio Grande and Pecos regions. In each of these regions, however, the projected acreage is much lower than when the demand model is solved using current practice costs.

In the Colorado and Great Basin regions—two of the four regions for which a decline is projected—the acreage of irrigated land projected for 1980 is below the 1954 level as well as the 1959 level. In the Upper Missouri and Upper Arkansas regions the 1980 figure is above the 1954 acreage but below the 1959 acreage.

The Equilibrium Model Solution

The equilibrium model solution is constructed by dropping from the demand model the equations used to project the national and regional output and adding a second identity equating the marginal value productivity of operating expenses to a specified cost or return level for operating expenses (see Tables 4 and 5). As in the case of the demand models, solutions are presented with the marginal value productivity of irrigated land equated to both current practice costs and full costs.

The simultaneous solution for equilibrium output and input levels produces results with greater variation from 1954 and 1959 levels of irrigated acreage and output than the solution of the demand projection models. Output growth is not limited by historical trends as in the demand models. In areas where the 1954 estimated marginal value productivity levels for irrigated land or operating expenses were high relative to the levels specified in the identity relationships, equilibrium solutions generally indicate sharp rises in output as well as in input. Where the marginal value productivity estimates were low relative to the specified levels, the solution generally indicates declines in output and input.

This effect is particularly apparent in the current practice solutions for the equilibrium model (Table 14, column 7). In some areas—the South Pacific and the Upper Rio Grande and Pecos, for example—the projected level of irrigated acreage clearly exceeds the available land resources of the region that are suitable for irrigation even if there were no constraints on the availability of water. These solutions represent, therefore, little more than an identification of the fact that estimates based upon current production functions do not take account of the rapidly diminishing quality of irrigable land in these particular regions. Also they point to the excess pressure for irrigation development that will result if capital and operating costs, including water charges, are held near current practice levels.

The full cost solutions of the equilibrium models indicate much lower levels of irrigated acreage than the demand model solutions in all western water resource regions. This indicates strikingly that the projected acreages are not consistent with economic optimization in view of current production functions and the levels of costs of inputs and outputs. The projections thus imply increased prices of outputs relative to inputs, notable gains in technological efficiency, or policies which maintain large amounts of economically inefficient irrigation. This illustrates the utility of the equilibrium model for spelling out implications of this character.

In six of the nine regions—Pacific Northwest, Colorado River, Great Basin, Western Gulf, Upper Arkansas-White-Red, and Upper Missouri—the full cost equilibrium solutions project a decline from 1954 and 1959 levels of irrigated acreage. In two other regions—Central Pacific and South Pacific—substantial increases in irrigated acreage are indicated even by the full cost solutions of the equilibrium model. In the Upper Rio Grande and Pecos region no solution is attempted. Here both current practice and full cost equilibrium solutions were rejected, as their "explosive" character indicated that the simultaneous solution imposes too heavy a burden on the accuracy of the statistically estimated coefficients of the model. In order to fill out the equilibrium model solution column of the table, the full cost demand model output projection and the U.S.D.A. high irrigated acreage projection were inserted for the Upper Rio Grande and Pecos region.

Irrigated land is, however, typically not withdrawn from production unless there is competition for water from economically attractive uses such as occur in areas of expanding industrial or urban demand. In other cases, low productivity in agriculture is more likely to be reflected in a revaluation of land prices than in rapid decline in irrigated acreage. In Chapter 3 it was pointed out that efficiency requires that a project continue to be used as long as marginal value product exceeds variable costs, including all opportunity costs. Some time is required in most cases for the short-run social optimum equilibrium position to approximate the long-run social optimum.

Should policy be adopted which would cause the irrigator to bear the full social costs of his irrigation, the full cost equilibrium solution serves as an indication of the direction of adjustment. As noted previously, the model does not form a basis for predicting the speed of this adjustment and accordingly for forecasting a specific irrigated acreage in 1980.

A specific projection for 1980 can, as indicated in Chapter 3, be extracted from the equilibrium model by imposing restrictions on the rate of adjustment toward the calculated equilibrium levels of irrigated acreage. On this basis a "restricted equilibrium" projection for 1980 has been constructed to deal with cases where (a) the equilibrium model solutions imply sharp declines in the acreage of irrigated land from 1959 levels; (b) competition between agricultural and nonagricultural uses appears to limit the growth of irrigated acreage; and (c) simultaneous solution of the model clearly places too heavy a burden on the estimated coefficients of the model. The results of these calculations are shown in Table 14, column 9. The full cost equilibrium model solutions imply sharp declines in irrigated acreage in six regions—the Pacific Northwest, Colorado River, Great Basin, Western Gulf, Upper Arkansas-White-Red, and Upper Missouri water resource regions. In these regions the restricted equilibrium projections were constructed by imposing a 10 per cent limit on the decline in irrigated acreage between 1959 and 1980 and solving the model for farm output, operating expense inputs, and the marginal value productivity of irrigated land.[2] The restricted equilibrium solutions permit somewhat higher levels of farm output and lower levels

[2] This procedure is similar to the method used to constrain the rate of adjustment toward the long-run equilibrium in the "recursive programming" technique In both cases the objective is to introduce a dynamic adjustment process into an equilibrium model. For applications of the "recursive programming" approach see R. H. Day, *Recursive Programming and Production Response* (Amsterdam: North-Holland Publishing Company, 1963); and W. N. Schaller, "A Recursive Programming Analysis of Regional Production Response" (Ph.D. thesis, University of California, September, 1962).

of marginal value productivity for irrigated land in these regions than the full cost equilibrium solutions.

In the two regions where a sharp rise in irrigated acreage is projected by the full cost solution—the Central Pacific and South Pacific water resource regions—competition between agricultural and other uses appears likely to limit the rate of expansion to below the projected level. In these two regions the full cost level was adjusted upward to reflect a higher opportunity cost for water in nonagricultural uses, and the model was again solved to obtain the equilibrium levels of farm output, irrigated acreage, and operating expenses. The projected annual amortization and associated costs on federal projects (Table 11) were adjusted upward by 50 per cent and the total amortization and associated costs were recomputed. The effect was to raise total amortization and associated costs per acre from $108.51 to $127.24 in the Central Pacific and from $275.58 to $352.03 in the South Pacific. Even though water is valued at the higher level, the equilibrium solution indicates sharp increases in both irrigated acreage and farm output in the two regions. These exercises illustrate the flexibility of the equilibrium model. If we arbitrarily accept these adjustments in opportunity costs and then make the further arbitrary assumption that the equilibrating process will have been completed by 1980, this procedure yields a figure for irrigated acreage at that date.

In the Upper Rio Grande and Pecos region, the full cost demand model output projection and the U.S.D.A. high irrigated acreage projections were inserted in the restricted column as in the case of the current practice and full cost equilibrium models.

In sum, column 9 represents the results of amended equilibrium calculations incorporating what may be some reasonable assumptions about opportunity costs and some much more arbitrary assumptions about rates of adjustment toward equilibrium. As already noted, these calculations and the resulting figures are to be considered illustrative of the way the equilibrium model could be used in the presence of fuller information. This having been said, it must also be noted that these projections contain fewer arbitrary elements and are much more sensible from an economic point of view than many requirements projections upon which important decisions have been based.

It may be of some interest in this connection to compare the results of the restricted equilibrium model with the projections of the Senate Select Committee on Water Resources. The latter indicate sharp competition between irrigation and nonagricultural uses by 1980 in five western water resource regions—South Pacific, Colorado River, Great Basin, Upper Rio Grande and Pecos, and Upper Missouri. In the five regions, projected requirements for all purposes exceed the maximum flow that can be maintained (Table 15). The restricted equilibrium projections reduce the deficit below the Senate Select Committee projections in the three regions where the marginal value productivity of irrigated land is relatively low—Colorado River, Great Basin, and Upper Missouri. In the two regions where the marginal value productivity of irrigated land is relatively high—the South Pacific and the Upper Rio

TABLE 15. Implications of Restricted Equilibrium Solutions for Water Losses in Five Deficit Water Resource Regions, 1980

(million gallons/day)

	Senate Select Committee projections			Computed irrigation losses			Adjusted deficit (based on restricted equilibrium model acreage) [4]
Region	Maximum flow that can be maintained [1]	Required flow [1]	Deficit [1]	Senate Select Committee projection [1]	Restricted equilibrium model solution [2]	Increase (+) or decrease (−) in loss [3]	
	(1)	(2)	(3)	(4)	(5)	(6)	(7)
South Pacific	320	10,600	10,280	3,312	5,322	+2,010	12,290
Colorado River	10,400	17,300	6,900	14,396	11,949	−2,447	4,453
Great Basin	9,300	12,100	2,800	6,698	4,890	−1,808	992
Upper Rio Grande and Pecos	950	7,300	6,350	4,964	5,465	+ 501	6,851
Upper Missouri	26,900	33,600	6,700	15,011	12,954	−2,057	4,643

[1] Columns (1) to (4) are from *Water Supply and Demand*, by Nathaniel Wollman, Committee Print No. 32, Select Committee on National Water Resources, U.S. Senate, 86th Congress, 2d Session (Washington: U.S. Government Printing Office, 1960), Tables 16 and 30. Agricultural losses are used to approximate irrigation losses since irrigation losses are not presented for 1980. Agricultural losses are computed assuming application of all the water the plant can beneficially use. Actual use in 1954 was almost 30 per cent below the level computed on this basis.

[2] Computed by assuming that water requirements will change in proportion to the difference between the U.S.D.A. medium and the restricted equilibrium acreage projections (see Table 17).

[3] Column (5) minus column (4).

[4] Column (3) plus column (6).

Grande and Pecos—the restricted equilibrium projections imply even greater deficits than those projected by the Senate Select Committee.

In evaluating the possibility of achieving the projected levels of irrigated acreage in western water resource regions, it is well to keep in mind that the agricultural losses reported by the Senate Select Committee were computed assuming that all the water that the plant can beneficially use would be applied. Application at such a level clearly exceeds the optimum economic level assuming water has a cost.[3] In 1954, actual use was almost 30 per cent below the level estimated using the maximum beneficial use procedure. In the South Pacific and the Upper Rio Grande and Pecos regions, where increases in acreage are projected in spite of growing deficits, realization of the levels of irrigation development projected in the restricted equilibrium models and the level of nonagricultural use projected by the Senate Select Committee will probably depend on increased importation of water from other water resource regions. The California Water Plan projects importation of water from the Central Pacific to the South Pacific region.[4] Diversion of water from the San Juan River (Colorado River water resource region) to the Upper Rio Grande and Pecos water resource region in New Mexico is also contemplated.[5]

IRRIGATED ACREAGE PROJECTIONS FOR EASTERN WATER RESOURCE REGIONS

Demand Model Projections

The demand model projections of irrigated acreage for the eastern water resource regions, as for the western regions, are constructed by extending the productivity model to include two equations which relate regional output growth to national output growth and an identity which equates the calculated marginal value productivity of irrigated land to the capital and associated operating costs per acre of irrigated land (see

[3] Christoph Beringer, *An Economic Model for Determining the Production Function for Water in Agriculture,* Giannini Foundation Research Report 240 (Berkeley: University of California, 1961). Also C. V. Moore, "A General Analytical Framework for Estimating the Production Function for Crops Using Irrigation Water," *Journal of Farm Economics,* Vol. 43 (November, 1961), pp. 876–88.

[4] California Water Resources Board, *Water Utilization in California,* California Water Resources Board Bulletin No. 2 (Sacramento, 1955).

[5] Allen V. Kneese, "Some Economic Effects of Alternative Water Use Patterns in New Mexico," in *Water: Measuring and Meeting Future Requirements* (Boulder: University of Colorado Press, 1961), pp. 147–56.

Tables 3 and 4). Solutions to the demand model are presented with the marginal value productivity equated to both a current practice level and a higher level reflecting a discount for uncertainty.

The current practice cost level has a somewhat different interpretation in the eastern water resource regions than in most western regions. Since most of the irrigation development in the East is "single enterprise" development there tends to be a much closer approximation between private and public costs and between current practice costs and anticipated development costs in the East than in the West. If there were no uncertainty with respect to the productivity of irrigated land, farmers in the eastern water resource regions could be expected to expand irrigated acreage until the marginal value productivity of irrigated land is equated to the current practice cost level.

Farmers in eastern water resource regions, however, are confronted, on the average, with a good deal more uncertainty with respect to the productivity of irrigated acreage than farmers in western water resource regions. In the East, greater variability of rainfall introduces a major source of uncertainty.[6] Furthermore, farmers and their advisors from the agricultural extension services and the irrigation equipment firms have typically accumulated less experience with irrigation and are not in as good a position to specify optimum irrigation practices in the East as in the West.[7]

[6] For data on variations in rainfall and differences in moisture see the series of publications on agricultural drought by von Bavel and associates: C. H. M. von Bavel and P. J. Verlinder, *Agricultural Drought in North Carolina,* Bulletin 122, N.C. Agricultural Experiment Station, 1956; C. H. M. von Bavel and J. H. Lillard, *Agricultural Drought in Virginia,* Bulletin 128, Virginia Agricultural Experiment Station, 1957; C. H. M. von Bavel, L. A. Forrest, and T. C. Peele, *Agricultural Drought in South Carolina,* S.C. Agricultural Experiment Station, 1957; C. H. M. von Bavel and J. R. Carnekar, *Agricultural Drought in Georgia,* Technical Bulletin N.S. 15, Georgia Agricultural Experiment Station, 1955. *Drought and Water Surplus in the Agricultural Soils of the Lower Mississippi Valley Area,* Technical Bulletin 1209, U.S. Department of Agriculture, Agricultural Research Service (Washington, 1959); R. S. Palmer, *Agricultural Drought in New England,* Technical Bulletin 97, New Hampshire Agricultural Experiment Station, 1958.

[7] According to D. W. Thomas and G. R. Slater *(Irrigation Costs and Returns, Southwestern Indiana, 1955,* Research Bulletin No. 668, Purdue University, Agricultural Experiment Station [Lafayette: August, 1958], p. 12), "The most striking feature of the irrigated crop yields obtained in these 23 farms in 1955 was the rather extreme field-to-field and farm-to-farm variations." Thomas and Slater indicate that many of these variations can be traced to lack of available research findings on which to base recommended management practices and lack of experience with irrigation by farm managers.

TABLE 16. Alternative Demand and Equilibrium Model Projections of Farm Output and Irrigated Acreage for Eastern Water Resource Regions

Region	Reported and estimated		1954 Demand model solution		1980 Demand model solution		1980 Equilibrium model solution with uncertainty adjustments
	1954	1959	Current practice cost	Uncertainty adjustments	Current practice cost	Uncertainty adjustments	
	(1)	(2)	(3)	(4)	(5)	(6)	(7)
Northeast							
Output (million $)	2,056		2,056	2,058	3,152	3,152	3,237
Irrigated land (thousand acres)	189	193	3,317	2,211	5,085	3,390	3,482
Productivity of							
Irrigated land ($/acre)	1,036.82		59.00	88.50	59.00	88.50	88.50
Operating expenses ($/$)	1.35						1.50
Great Lakes							
Output (million $)	1,788		1,788	1,788	2,800	2,800	1,797
Irrigated land (thousand acres)	51	71	831	554	1,300	867	557
Productivity of							
Irrigated land ($/acre)	1,013.22		62.00	93.00	62.00	93.00	93.00
Operating expenses ($/$)	1.19						1.50
Corn Belt							
Output (million $)	6,893		[1] 6,893	[1] 6,893	[1] 11,487	[1] 11,487	[1] 11,487
Irrigated land (thousand acres)	78	94	[1] 78	[1] 78	[1] 215	[1] 215	[1] 215
Productivity of							
Irrigated land ($/acre)	2,840.75						
Operating expenses ($/$)	0.90						
Southeast							
Output (million $)	2,286		2,286	2,286	3,399	3,399	3,326
Irrigated land (thousand acres)	123	157	1,530	1,020	2,275	1,517	1,444
Productivity of							
Irrigated land ($/acre)	806.77		65.00	97.50	65.00	97.50	97.50
Operating expenses ($/$)	1.78						1.50

TABLE 16—Continued.

	(1)	(2)	(3)	(4)	(5)	(6)	(7)
Florida							
Output (million $)	466		466	466	1,163	1,163	[2] 1,163
Irrigated land (thousand acres)	430	407	1,673	1,115	4,168	2,782	[2] 2,782
Productivity of							
Irrigated land ($/acre)	312.77		80.00	120.00	80.00	120.00	
Operating expenses ($/$)	2.86						
Lower Mississippi							
Output (million $)	904		904	904	1,487	1,487	[2] 1,487
Irrigated land (thousand acres)	536	446	819	547	1,348	901	[2] 901
Productivity of							
Irrigated land ($/acre)	169.00		111.00	166.00	111.00		
Operating expenses ($/$)	0.39						
Lower Arkansas-White-Red							
Output (million $)	651		651	651	859	859	1,302
Irrigated land (thousand acres)	598	506	3,035	2,023	4,009	2,672	4,050
Productivity of							
Irrigated land ($/acre)	243.69		48.00	72.00	48.00	72.00	72.00
Operating expenses ($/$)	1.41						1.50
Total (all eastern regions) [3]							
Output (million $)	15,044		15,044	15,044	24,346	24,346	23,799
Irrigated land (thousand acres)	2,002	1,874	11,282	7,549	18,399	12,343	13,430

[1] Neither demand nor equilibrium model projections were constructed for the Corn Belt because of the difficulty of obtaining significant regression coefficients for irrigated land (see Appendix 1). In the 1954 demand model, actual 1954 levels of irrigated acreage were accepted. The dampened trend output projection and the medium Department of Agriculture projection of irrigated acreage were accepted for the 1980 projection.

[2] Equilibrium model solutions were not attempted because of weakness of the coefficient for operating expenses. The uncertainty adjustment demand models were accepted for the two regions.

[3] Totals computed before rounding.

Sources: Column (1): Output and irrigated acreage were tabulated from sources identified in Table 6. Productivity estimates were calculated as indicated in discussion of the productivity model in Chapters 3 and 4. Column (2): Tabulations from 1959 Census of Agriculture and Irrigation supplied by Land and Water Branch, RDED, ERS, U.S. Department of Agriculture. Columns (3)–(7): See text discussion.

In an attempt to adjust for the impact of greater uncertainty in the eastern water resource regions the current practice cost estimates have been arbitrarily adjusted upward by 50 per cent.[8] The "uncertainty adjustment" demand model solutions for 1954 and 1980 presented in Table 16 are obtained by equating the marginal value productivity to this higher level.[9]

Solution of the demand models with capital and operating costs held at current practice levels resulted in a sharp increase in irrigated acreage from 1954 and 1959 levels in each eastern water resource region. A rise from 2 million acres in 1954 to 18.4 million acres in 1980 is projected for the entire region.

Solution of the demand models incorporating the uncertainty adjustment reduces the projected irrigated acreage by about one-third—from 18.4 million to 12.3 million acres. All regions continue to share in the projected rise in irrigated acreage, although the greatest increases are in the Northeast and Great Lakes regions where irrigated acreage was relatively small in 1954 and 1959.

Equilibrium Model Solutions

The empirical basis for equilibrium model solutions is weaker in the eastern than in the western water resource regions. Solutions were attempted for only four of the seven regions—Northeast, Great Lakes, Southwest, and Lower Arkansas-White-Red water resource regions. Solutions were not attempted for the Florida and the Lower Mississippi regions because of weakness in the coefficient for operating expenses. In order to fill out the column indicating equilibrium levels, the demand model projections using the uncertainty adjustment were inserted for

[8] For an attempt to evaluate the impact on returns to irrigation investment of variability of average weather conditions and variability due to the sequence of dry and wet years under North Carolina conditions see Shlomo Reutlinger and J. A. Seagraves, "A Method of Appraising Irrigation Returns," *Journal of Farm Economics,* Vol. 44 (August, 1962), pp. 837–50.

[9] Neither demand nor equilibrium model projections were constructed for the Corn Belt because of the difficulty of obtaining a statistically significant regression coefficient for irrigated land in the region (Appendix 1). In the 1954 demand model the actual 1954 level of irrigated acreage and output were accepted. The dampened trend output projection and the medium U.S. Department of Agriculture projection of irrigated acreage were accepted for all 1980 Corn Belt projections.

these two regions; and, as in the case of the demand model, the U. S. Department of Agriculture medium projections were used for the Corn Belt.

In view of the weaker empirical basis of the equilibrium solutions in the eastern water resource regions, only those based on an uncertainty adjustment are presented in Table 16. In two regions—the Northeast and the Southeast—the uncertainty adjustment demand model solutions are approximately the same as the equilibrium model solutions. In the Great Lakes area the equilibrium model solution indicates a considerably lower irrigated acreage and output by 1980 than the demand model projection. The implications of this type of situation were spelled out in some detail in the discussion of analogous instances in the western regions. In the lower Arkansas-White-Red region, the equilibrium solutions for output and acreage are considerably higher than the 1980 demand projections. In this instance, if relative prices and technology continue at present levels, and if the adjustment toward equilibrium is comparatively rapid, the 1980 demand projections may prove considerably too low. For what it may be worth in view of data uncertainties and the various arbitrarily injected acreages, the equilibrium model column indicates a slightly lower output and slightly higher acreage for all eastern water resource regions combined than does the demand model projection.

No attempt has been made to project a third "restricted equilibrium" model for eastern water resource regions. The empirical basis does not justify additional adjustments.

COMPARISON OF AGENCY AND MODEL SOLUTION PROJECTIONS

The demand projections and equilibrium model solutions for irrigated acreage in all the water resource regions are compared with projections prepared by the U.S. Department of Agriculture and the U. S. Bureau of Reclamation for the Senate Select Committee on National Water Resources and with actual acreage of irrigated land reported by the U. S. Census of Agriculture in 1954 and in 1959 in Table 17.

TABLE 17. Irrigated Acreage in 1954 and 1959 and Projections of Irrigated Acreage to 1980 for Western and Eastern Water Resource Regions

(Acres in thousands)

Region		Irrigated acreage reported		Department of Agriculture projections [3]			Bureau of Reclamation projections [4]	Model solution	
		1954 [1]	1959 [2]	Low	Medium	High		Demand [5]	Equilibrium [6]
		(1)	(2)	(3)	(4)	(5)	(6)	(7)	(8)
Pacific Northwest	(acres)	4,353	4,807	5,022	5,261	6,342	9,285	5,844	4,326
	(index)	100	111	115	121	146	213	134	99
Central Pacific	(acres)	6,064	6,300	6,875	6,869	6,266	13,565	10,928	14,581
	(index)	100	104	113	113	120	224	180	240
South Pacific	(acres)	789	737	827	816	921	1,000	2,257	1,311
	(index)	100	93	105	103	117	127	274	166
Colorado River	(acres)	2,813	3,025	3,283	3,280	3,327	3,990	1,674	2,723
	(index)	100	107	117	116	118	142	59	97
Great Basin	(acres)	1,936	1,830	2,242	2,257	2,315	2,245	1,229	1,647
	(index)	100	95	116	117	120	116	64	85
Upper Rio Grande and Pecos	(acres)	1,132	1,247	1,400	1,416	1,559	1,685	1,955	[7] 1,559
	(index)	100	110	124	125	138	149	173	138
Western Gulf	(acres)	4,432	4,785	5,022	5,126	6,350	5,070	7,137	4,306
	(index)	100	108	113	116	143	114	161	97
Upper Arkansas-White-Red	(acres)	1,409	2,388	1,626	1,681	2,081	2,570	1,698	2,149
	(index)	100	169	115	119	148	182	120	152
Upper Missouri	(acres)	4,622	6,029	5,500	6,287	9,118	10,800	4,668	5,426
	(index)	100	130	119	136	197	234	101	117
Total, western regions	(acres)	27,550	31,148	31,797	32,993	39,279	50,210	37,390	38,028
	(index)	100	113	115	120	143	182	136	138

TABLE 17—Continued.

		(1)	(2)	(3)	(4)	(5)	(6)	(7)	(8)
Northeast	(acres)	189	193	277	353	1,155		3,390	3,482
	(index)	100	102	147	187	612		1,796	1,845
Great Lakes	(acres)	51	71	79	112	778		876	557
	(index)	100	140	156	221	1,525		1,707	1,096
Corn Belt	(acres)	78	94	126	215	2,897		[8] 215	[8] 215
	(index)	100	121	162	276	3,733		276	276
Southeast	(acres)	123	157	385	462	2,580		1,517	1,444
	(index)	100	128	313	376	2,098		1,233	1,174
Florida	(acres)	430	407	505	657	960		2,782	2,782
	(index)	100	95	118	153	224		647	647
Lower Mississippi	(acres)	536	446	883	918	1,488		901	901
	(index)	100	83	165	171	278		168	168
Lower Arkansas-White-Red	(acres)	598	506	990	990	1,464		2,672	4,050
	(index)	100	85	166	166	245		447	677
Total, eastern regions	(acres)	2,002	1,874	3,245	3,707	11,322		12,343	13,430
	(index)	100	94	162	185	566		616	670
Total, all regions	(acres)	29,552	33,022	35,042	36,700	50,601		49,733	51,458
	(index)	100	112	119	124	171		168	174

[1] Tabulated from U.S. Bureau of the Census, *United States Census of Agriculture, 1954* (Washington: U.S. Government Printing Office, 1956).

[2] Tabulated from U.S. Bureau of the Census, *United States Census of Agriculture, 1959* (Washington: U.S. Government Printing Office, 1962).

[3] U.S. Department of Agriculture, *Land and Water Potentials and Future Requirements for Water*, Committee Print No. 12, Select Committee on National Water Resources, U.S. Senate, 86th Congress, 1st Session (Washington: U.S. Government Printing Office, 1960), pp. 71 (Table 44), 72 (Table 45), and 73 (Table 46). In the U.S.D.A. study Florida is treated as part of the Southeast. In this study the Florida projections are based on the following assumptions: (a) The high projections are based on a continuation of the 1949–54 rate of increase from 1954 to 1979; (b) The low projection is based on continuation of the 1949–54 rate of increase from 1959 to 1979; (c) The medium assumes that the increase will equal one-third the difference between the low and high projections. The projections for the entire Southeast region, including the Cumberland and the Tennessee river regions, were then obtained as a residual, after subtracting the Florida projections.

[4] U.S. Bureau of Reclamation, *Future Needs for Reclamation in the Western States*, Committee Print No. 14, Select Committee on National Water Resources, U.S. Senate, 86th Congress, 2d Session (Washington: U.S. Government Printing Office, 1960). The projection was constructed by adding (a) acres of newly irrigated land included in potential projections (Table 6, p. 11) to (b) estimated acreage irrigated in 1958 (p. 3). The Bureau of Reclamation did not make projections for eastern water resource regions.

[5] Data for western water resource regions from Table 14, column (6), full-cost solution; data for eastern water resource regions from Table 16, column (6), uncertainty adjustment solution.

[6] Data for western water resource regions from Table 14, column (9), restricted solution; data for eastern water resource regions from Table 16, column (7), uncertainty adjustment solution.

[7] U.S.D.A. high projection.

[8] U.S.D.A. medium projection.

The U.S. Department of Agriculture employed a requirements approach in constructing irrigated acreage projections. Total requirements for farm products in 1980 were based on projected population, continued improvements in level of diet, and projected levels of exports and imports. Three different total requirement levels were constructed on the basis of alternative population projections. Production requirements for crops, pasture, and product added by livestock were constructed for each population level. Projections of irrigated acreage requirements were then developed from the crop and pasture requirement projections. Regional allocations were based on an estimate of the suitability of land for irrigation in the several water resource regions. Projections were constructed for both 1980 and 2000.[10]

The Bureau of Reclamation projections represent physical potential rather than estimated requirements, and were made for western regions only. Estimates of irrigated acreage on 650 potential federal and 435 potential nonfederal projects were added to Bureau estimates of irrigated acreage in 1958 to arrive at the projections shown in Table 17. The potential projections clearly exceed the levels likely to be realized by either 1980 or 2000. The Bureau indicated, in its report to the Senate Select Committee, that 75 per cent of the federal projects and 90 per cent of the nonfederal projects could be developed by the year 2000. No requirements or other criteria were utilized to indicate the actual acreage of irrigated land that might be economically irrigated by 1980 or 2000.[11]

Between 1954 and 1959 irrigated acreage in the nine western water resource regions rose from 27.5 million to 31.1 million acres, an increase of 13 per cent. The Department of Agriculture projections for 1980 range from a low that is only slightly above the 1959 level to a high that indicates a 43 per cent increase from the 1954 level. The Bureau

[10] This brief summary does not do justice to the very complex series of steps employed in developing the regional projections of crop and pasture production and irrigated acreage. For additional detail see U.S. Department of Agriculture, *Land and Water Potentials and Future Requirements for Water* (Committee Print No. 12), Select Committee on National Water Resources, U.S. Senate, 86th Congress, 1st Session (Washington: U.S. Government Printing Office, 1960).

[11] For additional detail see U.S. Bureau of Reclamation, *Future Needs for Reclamation in the Western States* (Committee Print No. 14), Select Committee on National Water Resources, U.S. Senate, 86th Congress, 2d Session (Washington: U.S. Government Printing Office, 1960).

of Reclamation potential projection indicates a rise of 82 per cent from the 1954 level. The full cost demand model and the restricted equilibrium model solutions both project roughly the same level of irrigated acreage as the Department's high projection.

The demand model projections and the equilibrium model solutions indicate sharply different regional distributions of irrigated acreage than the agency projections.

Both the Department and the Bureau project the largest regional increases in irrigated acreage in the Upper Missouri water resources region, and substantial increases for the Pacific Northwest and the Upper Arkansas-White-Red water resource regions. The demand projection and the equilibrium model solution, on the other hand, both indicate declines from 1959 levels of irrigated acreage in the Upper Missouri and the Upper Arkansas-White-Red water resource regions. The demand model projection indicates a rise in the Pacific Northwest while the restricted equilibrium model solution indicates a decline.

Both the demand model projection and the equilibrium model solution do indicate sharply higher acreage and output in the Central Pacific and South Pacific water resource regions. The demand model solution indicates a similar pattern in the Upper Rio Grande and Pecos water resource region. In these three regions the model solutions exceed even the Bureau of Reclamation potential projections. In some instances, perhaps the Upper Rio Grande and Pecos is one, actual water shortage will of course keep irrigation expansion below this level.

In general, the differences between the agency projections and the solution of the models used in the present study reflect the heavier weight given to physical criteria in the agency projections and the heavier weight given to economic criteria in the model solution projections. Introduction of economic criteria which would limit expansion of irrigated acreage to situations where the marginal value productivity could be equated to capital and operating expenses would clearly act to restrict growth of irrigated acreages below physical potentials estimated by the two federal agencies in most western water resource regions. On the other hand, physical limitations which may not be adequately reflected in cost and productivity data used in the present study could hold expansion of irrigated acreage below the levels projected by the model solution in the Central Pacific, South Pacific, and Upper Rio Grande and

Pecos water resource regions. There would seem to be little doubt, however, that in these three regions the productivity of irrigated acreage is high enough to permit substantial expansion of irrigated acreage even at considerably increased water costs.

Between 1954 and 1959 irrigated acreage in the seven eastern water resource regions declined from 2 million acres to less than 1.9 million acres. The decline was concentrated in the three eastern regions that accounted for three-fourths of total irrigated acreage in the East in 1954—Florida, the Lower Mississippi, and the Lower Arkansas-White-Red regions. The Department of Agriculture low projection indicates an increase to approximately 3.2 million acres by 1980, slightly less than two-thirds higher than the 1954 level. The Department's high projection of 11.3 million acres by 1980 is more than five times as high as the acreage irrigated in 1954. The uncertainty adjustment demand projection and the equilibrium model solution (also based on uncertainty adjustment) both indicate an even greater increase. The equilibrium model solution is higher than the demand model projections primarily as a result of the high acreage indicated in the Lower Arkansas-White-Red water resource region.

The contrast between the high Department projection and both the demand model projection and the equilibrium solution is more pronounced at the regional level. Under the conditions that would make its high projection relevant, the Department anticipates the greatest relative rate of increase in irrigated acreage in the Corn Belt and Southeast water resource regions. The demand and equilibrium model solutions both indicate larger acreages than the Department anticipates by 1980 in the Northeast, Florida, and Lower Arkansas-White-Red regions. The U.S.D.A. high projection exceeds the equilibrium model projection but is less than the demand model projection. Both models indicate lower acreages than the high U.S.D.A. projection for the Southeast and the Lower Mississippi. The projection for the Corn Belt is not relevant to this comparison since the Department medium projection was inserted in the model solution columns for the Corn Belt.

Regardless of these differences, there is no disagreement with respect to the direction of change. All results indicate substantial increases in irrigated acreage in each eastern water resource region. This is in sharp contrast to the results obtained for the western water resource regions where the model solutions indicated declines in irrigated acreage in a number of water resource regions.

COMPARISONS BETWEEN ALL EASTERN AND WESTERN WATER RESOURCE REGIONS

The demand model solution projection indicates increases in irrigated acreage from 1954 levels of approximately 10 million acres each in the eastern and the western water resource regions. In the aggregate this is also about the acreage increase which would result from equilibrium adjustment in these areas based on solution of the equilibrium model. For the West, this is a smaller increase than the Department of Agriculture high projection and is considerably below the Bureau of Reclamation potential projection. For the East this acreage is considerably above the Department of Agriculture high projection.

The implication of the comparisons is that application of economic criteria of the type incorporated into the model solutions results in a greater shift in the expansion of irrigated acreage to the eastern regions than implied by the agency projections. In spite of the more rapid growth of irrigated acreage in the East in the demand model projection, the West would still account for approximately three-fourths of the nation's irrigated acreage in 1980.

A NOTE ON THE DEMAND FOR IRRIGATION WATER IN 1980

While the demand for irrigated land is clearly derived from the demand for farm output, the demand for irrigation water can be treated either as derived from the demand for irrigated land or as derived directly from the demand for farm output. If irrigation water is regarded as a strict complement to irrigated land, then it is clearly appropriate to treat the demand for water as derived from the demand for irrigated land and, for planning purposes, to project irrigation water requirements for specific alternative levels of irrigated acreage. If, on the other hand, an independent output response can be obtained for irrigation water while holding land input constant, the demand for irrigation water should be derived directly from the demand for farm output rather than from the demand for irrigated land, and the concept of irrigation water requirements for specific levels of irrigated acreage loses its validity as a planning tool.

The calculations on which the projections prepared for the Senate Select Committee are based carry the implicit assumption that irrigation water is a strict complement to irrigated land and that the demand for irrigation water is therefore derived from the demand for irrigated land. Calculations of water use are constructed by aggregating estimated water requirements per acre for individual crops modified to account for variations in efficiencies of application and delivery and, in the case of the projections by the Department of Agriculture, anticipated improvements in efficiency resulting from technological change. An assumption that the demand for water is derived from the demand for irrigated land is also employed here. Water was not entered directly into the production function but was treated as a complement to irrigated land. And in the cost estimates it is assumed that a constant quantity of water per acre is used in each region.

A substantial amount of research, based on procedures developed by Blaney and Criddle in the West and Thornthwaite in the East has been directed to the development of methods for estimating irrigation water "requirements" per acre for specified crops grown under specified climatic and soil conditions.[12] All of this work carries the assumption that the optimum amount of water "required" per acre can be defined in purely physical terms. Experimental data, particularly that developed by F. J. Veihmeyer and his associates in California, have been interpreted as supporting this assumption. Beringer, however, has shown that this experimental work, when re-interpreted within the framework of production economics, supports the hypothesis that crop response to incremental water inputs clearly is subject to the principle of diminishing marginal

[12] No attempt is made to review the extensive literature in this field. The basic documents are: Harry F. Blaney and Wayne D. Criddle, "A Method of Estimating Water Requirements in Irrigated Areas from Climatological Data," U.S. Department of Agriculture, Soil Conservation Service, Washington (rev. ed., 1950, mimeo.), and C. W. Thornthwaite, "An Approach Toward a Rational Classification of Climate," *Geographical Review,* Vol. 38 (1948), pp. 55–94.

productivity.[13] Thus, optimum application levels cannot be defined on the basis of purely physical criteria. Even at the enterprise or firm level an optimum can be defined only by equating the incremental costs and returns associated with the incremental output resulting from incremental water inputs. And at the macro or regional level where possibilities of substitution among enterprises and among geographic subareas exist the irrigation water "requirement" concept becomes even less valid as a planning tool than at the enterprise or firm level.[14]

However, attempts to work directly with the demand for irrigation water rather than irrigation water "requirements" for specified irrigated acreage levels have been relatively limited. Dawson's work in the Ainsworth, Nebraska area[15] and the work by Hartman and Anderson in Northeastern Colorado[16] are the only studies at the micro level that were identified. Attempts which have been made in this study to enter water as a separate variable in an aggregate regional production function have been unsuccessful.

It appears, therefore, that at present there is no alternative but to accept the requirement approach in relating water use to irrigated acreage in aggregate projections. In using it, however, it should be emphasized that for any given level of irrigated acreage the optimal application of irrigation water may vary widely depending on the incremental cost of water and the incremental return obtained from additional water. No attempt was made in this study to modify or test the specific irrigation water requirement projections contained in the reports to the Select Committee by the Department of Agriculture and the Bureau of Reclamation.

[13] Christoph Beringer, "Some Conceptual Problems Encountered in Determining the Production Function for Water," *The West in a Growing Economy* (Proceedings of the 32nd Annual Meeting of the Western Farm Economic Association, Logan, Utah, July 14-17, 1959), pp. 58–70. Also, *An Economic Model for Determining the Production Function for Water in Agriculture, op. cit.* See also, Charles V. Moore, "A General Analytical Framework for Estimating the Production Function for Crops Using Irrigation Water," *op. cit.*

[14] G. S. Tolley and V. S. Hastings, "Optimal Water Application: The North Platte River," *Quarterly Journal of Economics,* Vol. 74 (May, 1960), pp. 279–95.

[15] John A. Dawson, "The Productivity of Water in Agriculture," *Journal of Farm Economics,* Vol. 39 (December, 1957), pp. 1244–52.

[16] L. M. Hartman and R. L. Anderson, "Estimating the Value of Irrigation Water from Farm Sales Data in Northeastern Colorado," *Journal of Farm Economics,* Vol. 44 (February, 1962), pp. 207–13; and Raymond L. Anderson, "The Irrigation Water Rental Market: A Case Study," *Agricultural Economics Research,* Vol. 13 (April, 1961), pp. 54–58.

6

IRRIGATED ACREAGE PROJECTIONS AND IRRIGATION POLICY

Before discussing the irrigation policy implications of this study, the elasticity models are evaluated in terms of their operational validity. The actual levels of farm output and resource inputs that will be realized in 1980 will depend, in the main, on decisions that have not yet been made. The function of the projection model is not to predict these levels but to explore the consequences of alternative decisions as a guide to selection among alternative policies. The usefulness of a projection depends, therefore, not on whether the projection is actually realized but whether it contributes to correct policy and action. In many cases the correct policy or action will prevent the projection from being realized.

The degree by which a projection departs from a correct prediction will depend on three factors:[1] (1) the adequacy with which the relationships that are built into the projection model describe the behavior of that part of the economic system with which the analyst is concerned; (2) the accuracy with which the relationships in the economic model are estimated (in this study, the accuracy of the statistically estimated production functions); and (3) the accuracy with which the variables that enter from outside the system are estimated or projected—that is, the accuracy with which the equilibrium irrigation and operating expense cost estimates are projected in both models and the accuracy of the national and regional output projections in the demand model in this study.

In evaluating the projection models for policy analysis, major attention focuses on the possible effects of inadequate model specification and

[1] Tian Tong Tsui, "Forecasting Methodology and its Application to Land Price Forecasts" (Ph.D. thesis, Department of Agricultural Economics, University of Illinois, 1961), p. 24.

of incorrect statistical estimation. If model construction and parameter estimation are satisfactory, the policy implications can be explored by varying the levels or rates of change of the variables entered from outside the system.

EVALUATION OF ELASTICITY MODEL PROJECTIONS

The statistically estimated coefficients of the elasticity models appear to meet the test of significance and stability sufficiently well to permit demand model projections for all western water resource regions and equilibrium model solutions for all western regions except the Upper Rio Grande and Pecos. In addition, a restricted equilibrium model was developed which specified a gradual adjustment of the *ex post* social and private optimum toward the *ex ante* social optimum.

In the eastern water resource regions the statistically estimated coefficients of the elasticity models did not, in most regions, meet the tests of significance and stability as adequately as in the western water resource regions. The more limited role of irrigation in eastern agriculture and the variability of irrigation performance were apparently important factors in the relative weakness of the statistically estimated coefficients. The necessity of assuming stability in the estimated productivity coefficients at levels of irrigated acreage so far above 1954 levels creates additional problems, particularly for the results of the equilibrium model. In the eastern water resource regions, these disadvantages are great enough to vitiate in large part the results of the equilibrium models.

The demand model projection and equilibrium model solution for irrigated acreage for the two major regions and the nation as a whole are summarized in Table 18. Modification of these results could be obtained by expanding the model to permit explicit consideration of inputs other than irrigated land and output-increasing operating expenses and by changing the demand and technology assumptions that have been built into the model. It was not feasible to build such modifications explicitly into the models in this study. It is possible, however, to arrive at some judgments with respect to the changes which their explicit consideration would produce in the regional and national projections.

Additional inputs—labor, capital equipment, and nonirrigated land—are not incorporated into the equilibrium models because of the difficulty of obtaining statistically estimated coefficients that meet the significance and stability criteria (Appendix 1).[2] At the national level the primary effect of expanding the model to introduce these inputs would probably be to project a continuation of the rapid substitution of capital equipment for labor. Substantial modifications in the irrigated acreage and output projections could occur in regions where agricultural wage rates are well below long-run equilibrium levels. It seems likely that the irrigated acreage and farm output projections would be lower in the Central Pacific, South Pacific, Colorado River, Upper Rio Grande and Pecos, and Western Gulf regions if the effects of potential reductions in the flow of farm workers from Mexico were incorporated into the models. A shift toward more equal wage rates in the farm and nonfarm sectors would probably also lower the equilibrium solutions for the Southeast, Florida, Lower Mississippi, and Lower Arkansas-White-Red water resource regions. The net national impact could be a slight reduction in the equilibrium solution for output and irrigated acreage.

A second source of error in the models stems from use of the identities in the demand and equilibrium models as substitutes for factor supply functions. Use of the identities for this purpose implies that the supply of factors is perfectly elastic. This may not be too unrealistic for operating expenses, or even irrigated land, over the range projected in the eastern water resource regions. It is clearly not a valid assumption for irrigated land for those western water resource regions in which irrigated acreage is expected to expand. An attempt is made to overcome this deficiency by using the projected costs on federal, rather than nonfederal, projects and by developing the restricted equilibrium model. If it had been possible to develop operational supply functions for irrigated land, confidence in the precision of the solutions to both the demand and equilibrium models would be increased. Replacing the identities with supply functions would probably result in lower irrigated acreage projec-

[2] This issue is not relevant to the demand models since irrigated acreage is projected on the basis of the projected regional output, the marginal value product for irrigated acreage, and the identity relating irrigation cost to the marginal value product of irrigated acreage. Other inputs and technological change do not enter explicitly into the demand model.

tions in the demand models and both lower irrigated acreage and lower output in the equilibrium models.

More rapid growth in demand for farm output than projected in the demand model solutions would result in some combination of higher farm product prices, higher marginal value productivity of irrigated land, and increased acreage of irrigated land. Less rapid growth in demand than the projected output levels would result in some combination of lower farm product prices, lower marginal value productivity of irrigated land, and smaller acreage of irrigated land. For the projected levels of national output, however, a greater increase in output in any water resource region or group of regions must be accompanied by a smaller increase in output in some other region or regions.

The demand model solution projects a rise in farm output from an index of 100 in 1954 to 166 by 1980. Solution of the other model suggests an equilibrium level of output of 155 (see Table 18). The most recent Department of Agriculture farm output projections range from 155 to 168 (1954=100).[3] Since it seems unlikely that the demand for farm products will expand by less than 60 per cent between 1954 and 1980, the demand model projection may be the more realistic. It may, however, be associated with somewhat lower farm product prices and lower marginal value productivities for irrigated land relative to the mid-1950's.

Failure to provide explicitly for technological change in the demand and equilibrium models is perhaps the most serious source of bias. This could be taken care of in three ways. Where technological change occurs in a supply industry, it could be introduced through lower equilibrium cost estimates. Where it alters the marginal value productivity of a factor of production included in the production function, it could be introduced by modifying the productivity coefficient of the factor. And where it affects the productivity of inputs that are not specifically included in the function or that are neutral with respect to the inputs in-

[3] Rex F. Daly, "The National Environment for Business and Agriculture in the 1970's," paper presented at the Connecticut Cooperative Extension Conference, January 23, 1963, Storrs, Connecticut. Also U.S.D.A. Land and Water Policy Committee, *Land and Water Resources: A Policy Guide* (Washington: U.S. Department of Agriculture, May, 1962), pp. 36, 37.

TABLE 18. Summary of Farm Output and Irrigated Acreage Projections to 1980 for Western and Eastern Water Resource Regions

	Reported in 1954	1980 Demand model projection	1980 Equilibrium model solution
	(1)	(2)	(3)
Farm output			
Western water resource regions			
Value (million $)	9,595	16,463	14,375
Index (1954=100)	100	172	150
Eastern water resource regions			
Value (million $)	15,044	24,346	23,799
Index (1954=100)	100	162	158
Total (all regions)			
Value (million $)	24,639	40,809	38,174
Index (1954=100)	100	166	155
Irrigated acreage			
Western water resource regions			
Acres (thousand)	27,550	37,390	38,028
Index (1954=100)	100	136	138
Eastern water resource regions			
Acres (thousand)	2,002	12,343	13,430
Index (1954=100)	100	616	670
Total (all regions)			
Acres (thousand)	29,552	49,733	51,458
Index (1954=100)	100	168	174

Sources: (1) Output and acreage figures for 1954 were tabulated from sources identified in Table 6; (2) Table 14, column 6, and Table 16, column 6; (3) Table 14, column 9, and Table 16, column 7.

cluded in the function, it could be introduced by shifting the constant term of the production function.[4]

Technological change that results in either a decline in the equilibrium cost estimate or a rise in the productivity coefficient for irrigated land

[4] Attempts to develop an empirical basis for introducing shifts in the production function have been only partially successful. In J. C. Headley, "The Contribution of Supplemental Irrigation to Agricultural Output in the Eastern United States" (Ph.D. thesis, Department of Agricultural Economics, Purdue University, 1960), an attempt was made to utilize total productivity indexes developed for census regions to project the constant term in type-of-farming-region production functions (pp. 56–62). An attempt to estimate changes in the constant term statistically, however, indicated that it remained essentially unchanged between 1939 and 1954 in the California major irrigation counties. See V. W. Ruttan, "The Impact of Irrigation on Farm Output in California," *Hilgardia*, Vol. 31 (July, 1961), pp. 97, 108.

would produce higher irrigated acreage projections in the demand model and both higher irrigated acreage and output solutions in the equilibrium model.

A rise in the constant term of the production function would not affect the demand model projections. In the equilibrium model solution, however, it would permit a rise in output relative to both irrigated acreage and operating expenses. A shift comparable to that implied by the growth of total productivity in agriculture over the last decade and a half—by 2.0 per cent per year (Table 1)—would result in a more rapid growth of potential output than of demand. The effect would be a decline in farm product prices relative to factor prices and a decline in the demand for irrigated acreage relative to the equilibrium model solution.

It seems clear that expansion of the demand model to include both product demand functions and changes in technology would produce a 1980 output projection at least as high and perhaps higher than the level projected in the demand model. Similarly, explicit introduction of these factors into the equilibrium model would produce a solution at least as high as that actually obtained. The output projected by the demand model under these circumstances would have to be marketed at an even lower level of product prices relative to prices of production inputs than implied by the demand model projections. And the acreage of irrigated land utilized to produce the projected output levels would probably be lower and would certainly not exceed the levels indicated by the restricted equilibrium model solution for the western water resource regions and the uncertainty adjustment demand model solution for the eastern water resource regions.

IMPLICATIONS FOR ADDITIONAL RESEARCH

There are four main areas in which additional research should be focused in attempting to improve the empirical validity of the elasticity models and of projections derived from them. These include: (a) additional testing of the stability of coefficients in the regional production functions and the incorporation of technological change explicitly into the production functions; (b) estimation of regional supply functions for irrigated land; (c) evaluation of opportunity costs for water in non-irrigation uses for specific regions and subregions; and (d) modifications of the model to incorporate interregional as well as intraregional optimization criteria.

Regional Production Functions

Reliance on productivity coefficients estimated from data for a single year (1954) is perhaps the single most important limiting factor on the empirical validity of the marginal value productivity estimates and the projections of irrigated acreage presented in chapters 4 and 5. The stability of the productivity coefficients over time was examined only for California.[5] The coefficients were found to be surprisingly stable in the California study. Similar historical analysis should, however, be attempted for each of the other water resource regions.

Additional attempts should also be made to introduce technological change explicitly into the statistically estimated production functions. When the stability over time of the constant term of the statistically estimated function was examined for California it did not prove consistent with other observations of rapid increases in output per unit of total input in the Pacific type-of-farming regions.[6] And attempts to introduce total productivity adjustments into the constant term of the production function synthetically were not entirely satisfactory.[7] Since changes in technology can be reflected through shifts in the productivity coefficients and changes in the constant term of the function, an attempt should be made to estimate both simultaneously from the same set of observations.

The estimation of production functions and marginal value productivities at the regional level provides a general guide for ranking regions with respect to the potential for irrigation development. For individual project planning decisions, however, the marginal productivity of irri-

[5] V. W. Ruttan, *ibid.,* pp. 69–111.

[6] T. T. Stout and V. W. Ruttan, "Regional Patterns of Technological Change in American Agriculture," *Journal of Farm Economics,* Vol. 40 (May, 1958), pp. 196–207.

[7] J. C. Headley and V. W. Ruttan, "Regional Differences in the Impact of Irrigation on Farm Output," *Water Resources and Economic Development of the West,* Report No. 8, Committee on the Economics of Water Resource Development, Western Agricultural Economics Research Council (San Francisco, January, 1960), pp. 107–34.

gated land should be evaluated in relation to the cost of providing irrigation water and producing a crop at specific locations within major water resource regions. For this purpose the production functions should be estimated from data for specific farms or specific experimental trials within the prospective project area and not based on broad regional generalization.

Regional Supply Functions

In this study the regional marginal productivity estimates were equated to budgeted average cost levels in both the demand and equilibrium models. The precision of the projections would be increased if the cost identities, particularly the cost identity for irrigated land, could be replaced by factor supply functions.

A minimal step toward this objective is to approach the supply function through a use of alternative cost levels for successive increments of irrigated acreage in each water resource region. A reworking of the data on "new land equivalent construction cost" per acre developed for western water resource regions by the Bureau of Reclamation would represent a first step in such a project.[8]

In eastern water resource regions, the problem of estimating the incremental costs associated with additional acreage of irrigated land can probably best be approached by first constructing cost estimates for specific farms and specific locations utilizing a combination of survey and engineering cost data. As irrigation expands, however, and competition for water becomes more intense within agriculture and between agriculture and other uses, the individual farm approach will tend to break down, and a shift will have to be made to a watershed or river basin approach.

Opportunity Costs

In a market economy or an economy in which the allocation of water among alternative uses is based on the simulation of market criteria, the

[8] See U.S. Bureau of Reclamation, *Future Needs for Reclamation in the Western States* (Committee Print No. 14), Select Committee on National Water Resources, U.S. Senate, 86th Congress, 2d Session (Washington: U.S. Government Printing Office, 1960) pp. 15, 36–44, for "new land equivalent construction costs" per acre as estimated by the Bureau of Reclamation using "current practice" methods.

cost of water for irrigation use will depend not only on the supply function for irrigation water considered in isolation but upon the value of water in alternative uses. The studies of the Select Committee on National Water Resources indicated that in at least five western water resource regions—Upper Missouri, Upper Rio Grande and Pecos, Colorado, Great Basin, and South Pacific—competition among uses is expected to become severe on a basin-wide basis.[9] Competition among uses is also anticipated for limited areas within most water resource regions.

Even though the requirements approach utilized in the Select Committee Report projections tends to overstate the degree of competition among uses, such competition is a current reality in many areas and it can be expected to increase in the future. Where such competition is likely to develop, it is important to avoid water resource investment and development decisions which will direct water into the lower-valued uses. Increased attention should be given to attempts to project, for local areas, the impact of total area development on opportunity costs for irrigation water.

Interregional Equilibrium

From a national perspective, optimization of resource use among regions as well as within regions is an important objective. In the regional equilibrium model solutions presented in this study, the only formal procedures utilized to achieve interregional optimization were the identities which equated the calculated marginal value productivity levels with budgeted average cost levels for factor inputs and the implicit acceptance of product market prices in the marginal value productivity estimates. This procedure is probably satisfactory for operating expense items and farm products which are traded interregionally, but not for water.

Transfer of water from relatively low to high productivity regions—from the Colorado River to the South Pacific or the Upper Rio Grande and Pecos regions, for example, or from the Pacific Northwest to the Central Pacific—is normally brought about not by market processes but

[9] *Water Supply and Demand* (Committee Print No. 32), by Nathaniel Wollman, Select Committee on National Water Resources, U.S. Senate, 86th Congress, 2d Session (Washington: U. S. Government Printing Office, 1960), pp. 10–13, 47–52, 127.

by public investment decisions. The model should therefore be broadened to permit transfers of water from one region to another where the difference in the marginal value product is sufficient to cover transportation costs.

POLICY IMPLICATIONS AND CONCLUSIONS

Despite the limitations of the model and the qualifications of the empirical results discussed above, the "elasticity" framework advances the analysis of the potential demand for irrigated acreage a step beyond that achieved by reliance on the "requirements" and "physical potential" approaches. It provides an indicator of the acreage that would be irrigated in the several water resource regions of the United States under conditions in which full costs and returns govern irrigation development at the margin. The results, therefore, differ considerably from those obtained by the U.S. Department of Agriculture and U.S. Bureau of Reclamation projections for most regions. What then are the implications of the study for national policy with reference to investment in irrigation development?

Consider, first, the situation in the West where irrigation is most significant. Since before the turn of the century, state and federal agencies have assisted in the development of irrigated lands. Under the policies which evolved over more than half a century, federal funds have been provided for investment in irrigation development to an increasing extent where total costs to society have exceeded estimated net economic returns. As an essential corollary of this policy, the federal government has generously subsidized irrigation development through the provision of interest-free capital and the contribution of power revenues. Several justifications have been offered for these practices. It has been claimed that the nation had an important interest in the growth of the arid and semiarid West, and that investment in irrigation—even if not profitable on the basis of narrower economic criteria—could contribute to that growth. There has also been the justification that irrigation under federal policy provided additional opportunities for family farms and that such farm units gave strength to our national society.[10]

[10] See E. L. Peffer, *The Closing of the Public Domain* (Stanford: Stanford University Press, 1951), pp. 32–62; and Otto Eckstein, *Water-Resource Development* (Cambridge: Harvard University Press, 1958), pp. 192–236.

In recent years, however, greater emphasis has been placed upon the need to proceed with the development of irrigated lands to supply the food and fiber requirements of our growing population. This view was most notable in the Report of the President's Water Resources Policy Commission in 1950, and, despite the growth of farm surpluses, it is still reflected in statements supporting federal investment in western irrigation. It is often asserted, for example, that much of the production from irrigated lands is of a type that is not in surplus.

Projections based upon a "requirements" approach are of little if any help in considering irrigation policy issues of the type described above. Similarly, the elasticity projections set forth in this study do not add to our understanding of the extent to which irrigation development contributes to the nonagricultural development in the West or its subregions or of the importance of family farms. On the other hand, the elasticity projections do help illuminate the issue of whether it is essential to invest in irrigation facilities in which total costs exceed total monetary returns to society at current prices. These projections indicate that the food and fiber needs of the next several decades can be met by investing only in those irrigation facilities in which total costs are less than total returns based upon current prices. Although the projections can be considered only approximations, they are sufficiently valid to leave no doubt about this conclusion.

Emphasis has been placed upon the importance of irrigation in the production of specialty crops such as citrus fruits. It is significant that much western irrigation produces crops that, on the average, have a lower value than crops produced on irrigated land in eastern areas. This indicates that where cutbacks are projected the high-value crops need not necessarily be affected. In short, then, investment in irrigation facilities in which total costs exceed returns would be reflected in a net reduction in gross national product.

The question of whether irrigation should be subsidized poses a separate issue. These projections do not indicate whether subsidies to farmers in western water resource regions are desirable. It is apparent, however, that subsidizing a factor input such as water is a relatively inefficient form of income redistribution. Since a subsidy induces patterns of resource utilization which depart from the pattern that would result if farmers paid the full cost price for water, it inevitably involves inefficient resource use. Short-run departures from optimum resource use patterns induced in this manner would not be subject to such serious criticism if rapid expansion of irrigated acreage were needed to meet future food and fiber needs and if the water devoted to irrigation had few alternative uses. The fact is, however, that the food and fiber needs of the next several decades can be met without such subsidy and that important alternative uses for water are rapidly emerging in many areas in the West.

These results suggest the desirability of re-examining federal policy with reference to irrigation in the West. At a time when the nation is concerned about its rate of economic growth, it would appear questionable indeed to invest heavily in irrigation projects where costs exceed prospective returns. In other words, projects which depend upon secondary benefits and/or an unrealistic interest rate for justification are of dubious merit. This is particularly true in areas of the West where rapid urban growth competes for scarce water supplies. Additional costs will be imposed on society if it is found after a few years that such lands must be taken out of agricultural production to liberate water for other uses that are essential to the growth of the regional economy.

Although the projections are somewhat less reliable for the East than for the West, they indicate that a substantial growth in irrigation may be economically practicable in eastern water resource regions. Both the marginal value productivity of irrigated land and the average value of output per acre for irrigated land tend to be higher in eastern than in western water resource regions. This strongly suggests that agencies responsible for water resources planning and development should give careful consideration to irrigation potentialities in all areas of the nation.

For the most part there would appear to be little justification for investment in irrigation facilities where capital and operating costs cannot be fully repaid. Exceptions may occur where the objective of food and fiber production is superseded by some other objective, such as the development of a specific depressed area. Other than such exceptions, there would seem to be little basis for carrying projects which cannot meet the full cost criteria beyond the planning stage in anticipation of potential output requirements in the years beyond 1980. This is particularly true in view of the demonstrated difficulties of accurately forecasting the impact of future technological change on the rates of substitution among inputs and on the relationship between total inputs and output regardless of the projection model employed.

This is not to argue that planning to meet future contingencies is not desirable. There would seem to be a strong basis, however, for maintaining sufficient flexibility in resource planning to permit modification of development plans to incorporate the effects of unanticipated contingencies. The basis for delaying implementation of plans until market forces support the implications of projected costs and returns is even stronger. Public investment in irrigation is clearly a case where speed in decision-making may, by failing to take advantage of time as a resource, result in substantial waste of capital, labor, and physical resources; impose unnecessary adjustment burdens on the rest of agriculture; and dampen the rate of national economic growth.

APPENDICES

1. *Alternative Resource Productivity Coefficients and Factor Marginal Value Productivity Estimates for Water Resource and Farming Regions*

2. *Total and Average Farm Output and Input Measures for Water Resource Regions*

3. *National and Regional Farm Output Projections*

APPENDIX 1.

Alternative Resource Productivity Coefficients and Factor Marginal Value Productivity Estimates for Water Resource and Farming Regions

FACTOR PRODUCTIVITY COEFFICIENTS FOR WATER RESOURCE REGIONS

The factor productivity coefficients for the three Pacific water resource regions are presented in Table A1.1.

In the *Pacific Northwest* the productivity coefficients for irrigated land, nonirrigated cropland, and current operating expenses are stable over all three models and for farm workers over the last two models. Furthermore, the marginal productivities estimated are in quite close agreement at both the arithmetic and geometric means for the three equations. There would seem to be little basis for preferring the results of equations (2) or (3) rather than equation (1).

In the *Central Pacific* region the productivity coefficients are less stable than in the Pacific Northwest. Furthermore, the marginal productivity of irrigated land appears to be somewhat low and the marginal productivity of nonirrigated cropland relatively high compared to other estimates for this same general area.[1] Utilization of the water resource region as a basis for analysis appears to be a major source of difficulty. The Central Pacific region includes counties with both extremely low and relatively high annual rainfall and with wide variation in altitude and in growth conditions. As a result, the productivity coefficients for irrigated land appear to be lower and the productivity coefficients for nonirrigated cropland higher than if the coefficients were computed only for those

[1] V. W. Ruttan, "The Impact of Irrigation on Farm Output in California," *Hilgardia,* Vol. 31 (July, 1961), pp. 80–81.

TABLE A1.1. Alternative Factor Productivity Coefficients for Major Irrigation Counties in Three Pacific Water Resource Regions, 1954

Water resource region and equation		Constant term (in $\log_{10}$) a_0	All farm workers X_1	Machinery investment X_2	Livestock investment X_3	Irrigated land X_4	Non-irrigated cropland X_5	Current operating expense X_6	Sum of coefficients	Coefficient of determination R^2	Standard error of estimate (in $\log_{10}$) $\bar{S}$
Pacific Northwest (N=106)	(1)	1.4755	.3003†	.1367‡	−.0576‡	.2349*	.2383*	.2993*	1.1520	.8158	.1879
			(.1518)	(.1962)	(.1076)	(.0513)	(.0399)	(.0806)			
	(2)	1.8168	.3867*	—	−.0192‡	.2339*	.2457*	.3011*	1.1481	.8149	.1884
			(.0913)	—	(.0925)	(.0514)	(.0390)	(.0808)			
	(3)	1.7516	.3860*	—	—	.2281*	.2443*	.2966*	1.1549	.8148	.1884
			(.0912)	—	—	(.0428)	(.0384)	(.0777)			
Central Pacific (N=42)	(1)	1.5900	.3470*	.1392‡	−.1298‡	.2098*	.1695*	.4017*	1.1375	.9665	.1146
			(.1225)	(.1406)	(.0990)	(.0658)	(.0529)	(.1123)			
	(2)	1.9746	.3948*	—	−.1143‡	.2463*	.1707*	.4202*	1.1179	.9657	.1159
			(.1176)	—	(.0985)	(.0588)	(.0535)	(.1133)			
	(3)	1.6137	.4218*	—	—	.2222*	.1590*	.3650*	1.1679	.9645	.1179
			(.1191)	—	—	(.0531)	(.0524)	(.0990)			
(N=25)	(F2)	1.7886§	.0968	—	—	.3485	.0093	.4521	.9067	.9218	.1910§
			(.1189)	—	—	(.0726)	(.0190)	(.0803)			
South Pacific and Colorado (N=56)	(1)	0.8071	.2618*	.1364‡	.1577†	.0555‡	−.0134‡	.5085*	1.1064	.9700	.1254
			(.1022)	(.1674)	(.0835)	(.0769)	(.0165)	(.0964)			
	(2)	1.2085	.3035*	—	.1508†	.1041*	−.0065‡	.5337*	1.0857	.9696	.1262
			(.0914)	—	(.0833)	(.0506)	(.0142)	(.0941)			
	(3)	1.8862	.3119*	—	—	.1163*	−.0016‡	.5739*	1.0005	.9677	.1301
			(.0941)	—	—	(.0521)	(.0144)	(.0970)			
South Pacific (N=7)	(6)	3.0501	.0952‡	—	—	.5449†	—	.2369‡	.8770	.7756	.1190
			(.3708)	—	—	(.3164)	—	(.2621)			
	(7)	2.9332	—	—	—	.5698†	—	.2893†	.8591	.7707	.1042
						(.2637)		(.1440)			

* Significant at 0.05 level.
† Significant at 0.20 level.
‡ Not significant at 0.20 level.
§ Constant term and standard error of estimate in $\log_e$.

Note: Figures in parentheses represent standard error of productivity coefficients. Equation numbers preceded by "F" refer to type-of-farming regions.

counties which account for a major share of the irrigation in the Central Pacific region. The coefficients and marginal productivity estimates for equation (F2), which was computed from data for the 25 California counties with more than 50,000 acres of irrigated cropland in 1956, gives some indication of the impact of this wide diversity on the productivity estimates. In fact, equation (F2) appears to provide a better basis than the other equations for estimation of the marginal value productivities for the Central Pacific region.

The small number of counties in the *South Pacific* region creates a number of problems in estimating the productivity coefficients. With only seven counties in the area, the number of independent variables must be limited to two or three, as in equations (6) and (7), if sufficient degrees of freedom are to be preserved to assure statistical significance for the resulting coefficients. On the other hand, if the South Pacific region is combined with the Central Pacific or the Colorado River region in an attempt to meet the statistical requirements, the wide variations in growing conditions could have the same kind of effects on the productivity coefficient that were objected to in the Central Pacific region. The best solution to this problem would appear to be to accept the results of equation (7).

In the three Southern Mountain regions the coefficient for nonirrigated cropland is typically negative or not significant (see Table A1.2). It seems reasonable to expect low or nonsignificant coefficients for nonirrigated cropland in these predominantly desert regions even in normal years. The negative coefficients probably reflect the exceptionally low rainfall in these areas during the early 1950's. Water shortages were sufficient to bring about substantial declines in irrigated land between 1949 and 1954 in parts of Nevada, Utah, Colorado, New Mexico, and Wyoming.

In the *Colorado River* region the coefficient for irrigated cropland is not significant at an acceptable level in equation (1). The coefficient for current operating expenses is essentially the same in equation (2) as in equation (1). Elimination of the livestock investment variable in equation (3), however, appears to introduce considerable specification bias in the coefficient for current operating expenses. It would appear, therefore, that the coefficient of equation (2) provides a better basis for esti-

TABLE A1.2. Alternative Factor Productivity Coefficients for Major Irrigation Counties in Three Southern Mountain Water Resource Regions, 1954

Region and equation		Constant term (in $\log_{10}$) a_0	All farm workers X_1	Machinery investment X_2	Livestock investment X_3	Irrigated land X_4	Non-irrigated cropland X_5	Current operating expense X_6	Sum of coefficients	Coefficient of determination R^2	Standard error of estimate (in $\log_{10}$) $\bar{S}$
Colorado River	(1)	.6521	.2992*	.0743‡	.2970*	.0635‡	−.0324†	.4220*	1.1236	.9599	.1169
(N=49)			(.1019)	(.1623)	(.1131)	(.0751)	(.0189)	(.1041)			
	(2)	.8668	.3219*	—	.2968*	.0904†	−.0295†	.4323*	1.1119	.9597	.1172
			(.0910)	—	(.1133)	(.0477)	(.0178)	(.1027)			
	(3)	1.9033	.3193*	—	—	.0986†	−.0044‡	.5816*	.9957	.9530	.1266
			(.0963)	—	—	(.0515)	(.0161)	(.1075)			
Great Basin	(1)	.4104	.1846‡	.3784‡	.4527‡	−.0171‡	−.0194‡	.1977	1.1769	.9542	.9653
(N=39)			(.1226)	(.1667)	(.1531)	(.1142)	(.1895)	(.0976)			
	(2)	1.0461	.3792*	—	.4038*	.0698‡	.0007‡	.2390*	1.0926	.9470	.1038
			(.1130)	—	(.1572)	(.1173)	(.0180)	(.1050)			
	(3)	2.0572	.2889*	—	—	.3505*	.0151‡	.3436*	.9981	.9358	.1142
			(.1088)	—	—	(.0882)	(.0192)	(.1138)			
Upper Rio Grande and Pecos	(1)	1.0971	.3130*	−.1543‡	.1564‡	.3850*	−.0594†	.5179*	1.1587	.9198	.1504
(N=38)			(.1141)	(.2296)	(.1339)	(.1538)	(.0312)	(.1396)			
	(2)	.6587	.3122*	—	.1655‡	.3087*	−.0662*	.4766*	1.1968	.9188	.1514
			(.1146)	—	(.1343)	(.0979)	(.0301)	(.1215)			
	(3)	1.3293	.3270*	—	—	.2930*	−.0569†	.5467*	1.1098	.9153	.1546
			(.1171)	—	—	(.0973)	(.0292)	(.1176)			

* Significant at 0.05 level.
† Significant at 0.20 level.
‡ Not significant at 0.20 level.

Note: Figures in parentheses represent standard error of productivity coefficients.

mating the marginal value productivities than the coefficients of either equation (1) or (3). The high marginal productivity estimate for operating expenses and the low marginal productivity estimate for irrigated land may also imply considerable bias in the coefficients for equation (2).

In the *Great Basin* the coefficient for irrigated cropland is not significant at acceptable levels in either equation (1) or (2). The coefficient for irrigated land achieves an acceptable level of significance only when livestock investment is dropped from the equation. This apparently reflects the close relationship between livestock production and forage crop production in much of the Great Basin. It appears, therefore, that the coefficients from equation (3) provide a better basis for estimating marginal value productivities than the coefficients of either equation (1) or (2).

In the *Upper Rio Grande and Pecos* the coefficient for irrigated cropland declines sharply when the machinery investment variable is dropped. There would seem, however, to be little basis for selecting the coefficients from either equation (2) or (3) rather than equation (1) as bases for constructing the marginal value productivity estimates.

The coefficient for machinery investment is significant in each of the three Great Plains water resource regions (Table A1.3). In the *Western Gulf* the coefficients for the other variables show a high degree of stability after machinery investment is dropped from the equation. Since the coefficient for machinery investment is significant at an acceptable level and does not completely obscure the effect of variation in the other variables, however, the coefficients of equation (1) appear to provide the best base for constructing the productivity estimates.

In the *Upper Arkansas-White-Red River* region the coefficient for irrigated land is quite stable over all three equations. The other coefficients show some instability, particularly when machinery investment is dropped. There seems to be little reason for not choosing the coefficients of equation (1) as the basis for the marginal value productivity estimates.

In the *Upper Missouri* region machinery investment is so highly interrelated with the other variables in the equation that it appears to obscure any independent impact which they might exert on output in equation (1). The other variables are quite stable in equations (2) and (3).

TABLE A1.3. Alternative Factor Productivity Coefficients for Major Irrigation Counties in Three Great Plains Water Resource Regions, 1954

Region and equation		Constant term (in log_{10}) a_0	All farm workers X_1	Machinery investment X_2	Livestock investment X_3	Irrigated land X_4	Non-irrigated cropland X_5	Current operating expense X_6	Sum of coefficients	Coefficient of determination R^2	Standard error of estimate (in log_{10}) $\overline{S}$
Western Gulf	(1)	.7195	−.0500‡	.5386*	−.0920‡	.2926*	.1580*	.1552†	1.0852	.8871	.1375
(N=75)			(.0975)	(.1683)	(.0943)	(.0469)	(.0530)	(.0896)			
	(2)	2.0515	.1271†	—	−.0051‡	.3547*	.2768*	.2802*	1.0337	.8690	.1481
			(.0903)	—	(.1016)	(.0504)	(.0503)	(.0921)			
	(3)	2.0331	.1277†	—	—	.3549*	.2770*	.2770*	1.0366	.8690	.1480
			(.0894)	—	—	(.0502)	(.0502)	(.0662)			
Upper Arkansas-White-Red	(1)	1.4656	.0974†	.2566*	−.0632‡	.1242*	.3012*	.2962*	1.0125	.9086	.1032
(N=81)			(.0613)	(.1114)	(.0932)	(.0268)	(.0470)	(.0872)			
	(2)	2.4522	.1787*	—	−.1153‡	.1331*	.3514*	.3821*	.9301	.9021	.1068
			(.0553)	—	(.0944)	(.0277)	(.0472)	(.0860)			
	(3)	2.1125	.1956*	—	—	.1323*	.3428*	.3085*	.9792	.9002	.1078
			(.0547)	—	—	(.0279)	(.0460)	(.0569)			
Upper Missouri	(1)	.1501	−.1915†	.9112*	−.0145‡	.0335*	.0830*	.1756*	.9974	.8671	.1030
(N=154)			(.1127)	(.1346)	(.0476)	(.0166)	(.0263)	(.0382)			
	(2)	2.7191	.5623*	—	.0852†	.0919*	.1655*	.0967*	1.0015	.8103	.1230
			(.0863)	—	(.0554)	(.0191)	(.0308)	(.0415)			
	(3)	3.1334	.5962*	—	—	.1020*	.1663*	.0983*	.9629	.8073	.1240
			(.0855)	—	—	(.0184)	(.0311)	(.0419)			

* Significant at 0.05 level.
† Significant at 0.20 level.
‡ Not significant at 0.20 level.

Note: Figures in parentheses represent standard error of productivity coefficients.

Table A1.4. Alternative Factor Productivity Coefficients for Major Irrigation Counties in Three Northern Water Resource Regions, 1954

Region and equation		Constant term (in $\log_{10}$) a_0	All farm workers X_1	Machinery investment X_2	Livestock investment X_3	Irrigated land X_4	Non-irrigated cropland X_5	Current operating expense X_6	Sum of coefficients	Coefficient of determination R^2	Standard error of estimate (in $\log_{10}$) $\bar{S}$
Northeast	(1)	2.6723	.0714‡	.5997*	−.1469*	.0952*	−.1117*	.5090*	1.0167	.9397	.0902
(N=59)			(.1175)	(.1509)	(.0542)	(.0411)	(.0548)	(.0927)			
	(2)	2.1868	.4297*	—	−.0989‡	.1013*	.0528‡	.5156*	1.0005	.9135	.1071
			(.1217)	—	(.0599)	(.0483)	(.0475)	(.1005)			
	(3)	2.0082	.3828*	—	—	.1181*	.0251‡	.4832*	1.0092	.9088	.1089
			(.1045)	—	—	(.0459)	(.0448)	(.0698)			
Great Lakes	(1)	3.2868	.3284‡	.1693‡	−.2204‡	.0765‡	.2963‡	.2636‡	.9138	.7320	.1026
(N=25)			(.2676)	(.5082)	(.2007)	(.1102)	(.2497)	(.2210)			
	(2)	3.3651	.3889†	—	−.2407‡	.0828‡	.3393†	.2938†	.8640	.7303	.1002
			(.1982)	—	(.1880)	(.1063)	(.2124)	(.1990)			
	(3)	3.5037	.3713†	—	—	.1198‡	.1722‡	.1517‡	.8149	.7049	.1065
			(.1877)	—	—	(.1072)	(.1630)	(.1640)			
(N=155)	(F1)	.8731§	−.0464‡	.4450*	—	.0288*	.2522†	.2846*	1.0644	.9088	.2839§
			(.1257)	(.1619)	—	(.0217)	(.0828)	(.0682)			
Corn Belt	(1)	2.8996	−.0201‡	.3498†	−.0576‡	.1079‡	.1054‡	.4071*	.8726	.8285	.1032
(N=35)			(.1420)	(.1611)	(.1301)	(.0845)	(.1729)	(.1814)			
	(2)	2.3691	.0418‡	—	−.0178‡	.0994‡	.0791‡	.6160*	.8184	.7984	.1100
			(.1485)	—	(.1369)	(.0892)	(.1832)	(.1835)			
	(3)	2.3602	.0333‡	—	—	.0993‡	.0717‡	.6095*	.8137	.7983	.1081
			(.1308)	—	—	(.0858)	(.1708)	(.1324)			
	(F1)	.2047§	−.2134*	.9153*	—	.0313*	.3327*	.1866*	1.2526	.8901	.2464§
			(.0601)	(.0577)	—	(.0132)	(.0474)	(.0445)			

* Significant at 0.05 level.
† Significant at 0.20 level.
‡ Not significant at 0.20 level.
§ Constant term and standard error of estimate in $\log_e$.

Note: Figures in parentheses represent standard error of productivity coefficients. Equation numbers preceded by "F" refer to type-of-farming regions.

Equation (2) is used as the basis for constructing the marginal value productivity estimates.

In the *Northeast* the negative coefficient for nonirrigated land and the low coefficient for employment in equation (1) appear to reflect the close relationship between machinery investment and these two variables (see Table A1.4). The coefficient for farm workers is higher in equation (2) where the machinery investment variable is dropped, but the coefficient for nonirrigated cropland still does not achieve an acceptable level of significance, although it does exceed its standard error. Equation (1) appears, nevertheless, to provide a suitable basis for estimation of the marginal value productivities for irrigated cropland and current operating expenses.

None of the equations computed for the *Great Lakes* region appear to provide an acceptable basis for computing marginal productivity estimates. The failure to achieve an acceptable level of statistical significance for most of the coefficients in the equations appears to reflect the limited number of major irrigation counties and the wide diversity in agricultural production among counties in the region. Equation (F1), computed for all major and limited irrigation counties in the Great Lakes type-of-farming region, does appear on statistical grounds to provide a better basis for constructing marginal value productivity estimates for irrigated cropland, nonirrigated cropland, and current operating expenses.

The situation in the *Corn Belt* is similar to that in the Great Lakes region. Except for current operating expenses, the coefficients are typically not significant at acceptable levels. Again this appears to reflect the wide diversity in the agriculture of counties in the region (when defined in terms of watershed boundaries) and the limited number of major irrigation counties in the region. Equation (F1), computed for all major and limited irrigation counties in the Corn Belt type-of-farming region, appears on statistical grounds to provide a better basis for calculating marginal value productivity estimates for irrigated cropland, nonirrigated cropland, and current operating expenses. The strong interaction between machinery investment and farm workers precludes a meaningful estimate of the marginal productivities of these two factors, however.

TABLE A1.5. Alternative Factor Productivity Coefficients for Major Irrigation Counties in Four Southern Water Resource Regions, 1954

Region and equation		Constant term (in $\log_{10}$) a_0	All farm workers X_1	Machinery investment X_2	Livestock investment X_3	Irrigated land X_4	Non-irrigated cropland X_5	Current operating expense X_6	Sum of coefficients	Coefficient of determination R^2	Standard error of estimate (in $\log_{10}$) $\overline{S}$
Southeast	(1)	3.0822	.3822*	.1733†	−.2803*	−.0524‡	.1865†	.4471*	.8604	.8198	.1311
(N=70)			(.1067)	(.1040)	(.1271)	(.0871)	(.1024)	(.1355)			
	(2)	2.7776	.4493*	—	−.2777*	−.0545‡	.2181*	.5187*	.8539	.8111	.1332
			(.1048)	—	(.1288)	(.0884)	(.1032)	(.1347)			
	(3)	2.1398	.4505*	—	—	−.0758‡	.0787‡	.4618*	.9152	.7963	.1373
			(.0911)	—	—	(.0903)	(.0800)	(.1188)			
(N=213)	(F1)	.6911§	.1890*	.1674*	—	.0435*	.2214*	.4645*	1.0856	.8562	.2766§
			(.0427)	(.0570)	—	(.0171)	(.0457)	(.0446)			
Florida	(1)	1.5551	.1141‡	.0277‡	−.0931‡	.2871*	.1258*	.6148*	1.0763	.9175	.1322
(N=41)			(.1704)	(.2233)	(.1012)	(.0858)	(.0662)	(.1662)			
	(2)	1.5384	.1308†	—	−.0917‡	.2893*	.1268†	.6175*	1.0728	.9175	.1303
			(.1028)	—	(.0991)	(.0829)	(.0648)	(.1627)			
	(3)	1.1733	.1345†	—	—	.2783*	.1098†	.6007*	1.1234	.9154	.1301
			(.1001)	—	—	(.0658)	(.0583)	(.1233)			
Lower Mississippi	(1)	2.7305	.1937*	−.0097‡	−.2320*	.1006*	.8570*	.0424‡	.9521	.9615	.0684
(N=52)			(.0656)	(.0557)	(.0590)	(.0267)	(.1543)	(.0839)			
	(2)	2.7460	.1934*	—	−.2305*	.0989*	.8481*	.0419‡	.9518	.9615	.0677
			(.0649)	—	(.0576)	(.0242)	(.1428)	(.0830)			
	(3)	2.1172	.1582*	—	—	.1314*	.9034*	−.1342†	1.0588	.9409	.0829
			(.0709)	—	—	(.0223)	(.0835)	(.0916)			
Lower Arkansas-White-Red	(1)	.6644	.4880*	.0694†	.0684‡	.2239*	.0609‡	.4200*	1.3306	.9374	.0834
(N=43)			(.1108)	(.0548)	(.1232)	(.0515)	(.1173)	(.0974)			
	(2)	.4441	.4976*	—	.0613‡	.2372*	.1168‡	.4401*	1.3530	.9345	.0841
			(.1114)	—	(.1241)	(.0520)	(.1113)	(.0982)			
	(3)	.6682	.5141*	—	—	.2246*	.1250‡	.4568*	1.3205	.9340	.0833
			(.0672)	—	—	(.0228)	(.1073)	(.0567)			

* Significant at 0.05 level.
† Significant at 0.20 level.
‡ Not significant at 0.20 level.
§ Constant term and standard error of estimate in $\log_e$.

Note: Figures in parentheses represent standard error of productivity coefficients. Equation numbers preceded by "F" refer to type-of-farming regions.

Significant relationships between factor inputs and output were obtained more frequently for the southern than for the northern water resource regions in the East (see Table A1.5).

The *Southeast* is the major exception to this generalization. As in the case of the Great Lakes and the Corn Belt, equation (F1), computed for the Southeast type-of-farming region, appears to meet the statistical criteria better than any of the equations computed for the Southeast water resource region.

In *Florida* the coefficients for irrigated land, nonirrigated land, and current operating expenses are quite stable across all three equations. The marginal value productivity estimates computed for Florida are based on the coefficients for equation (1).

In the *Lower Mississippi* region the coefficient for irrigated cropland, although not as stable as might be desired, meets the criteria for statistical significance in all three equations. A strong association between nonirrigated cropland and current operating expenses appears to obscure the independent influence of these two variables on output, however. The coefficients for the Delta type-of-farming region do not provide an acceptable base for computing factor marginal productivity estimates, since the Delta also includes most of the counties in the Lower Arkansas-White-Red water resource region. The coefficient for irrigated cropland from equation (1) is used in the marginal value productivity estimates.

In the *Lower Arkansas-White-Red Rivers* water resource region the coefficients for irrigated land and current operating expenses are relatively stable and satisfy the criteria for statistical significance. The coefficient for nonirrigated cropland does not satisfy either requirement. The coefficients from equation (1) are used in constructing the marginal productivity estimate for irrigated land and current operating expenses.

FACTOR PRODUCTIVITY COEFFICIENTS FOR TYPE-OF-FARMING REGIONS

The factor productivity coefficients for the thirteen type-of-farming regions are presented in Tables A1.6 to A1.11. In general, the productivity coefficients for the type-of-farming regions meet the significance and stability requirements better than the coefficients for the water resource regions. This appears to reflect greater homogeneity of resource-use patterns and productivity in these regions than in the water resource regions.

FACTOR MARGINAL VALUE PRODUCTIVITY ESTIMATES

The complete set of factor marginal value productivity estimates are presented in Tables A1.12 and A1.13. These were calculated using (a) the resource productivity coefficients of Tables A1.1 to A1.11, and (b) the arithmetic and geometric average factor input levels of Appendix 2.

TABLE A1.6. Alternative Resource Productivity Coefficients for Irrigation Counties in the Pacific Type-of-Farming Regions, 1954

Region and equation	Constant term (in $\log_e$) a_0	All farm workers X_1	Livestock investment X_3	Irrigated cropland X_4	Non-irrigated cropland X_5	Current operating expense X_6	Sum of coefficients	Coefficient of determination R^2	Standard error of estimate (in $\log_e$) $\overline{S}$
Northwest [1]									
(1)	.2225	.4346	−.1865	.2353	.3316	.2035	1.0186	.7852	.4130
	—	(.0876)	(.0967)	(.0468)	(.0418)	(.0827)	—	—	—
(2)	.1704	.4374	—	.1849	.3143	.1623	1.0989	.7712	.4225
	—	(.0207)	—	(.0192)	(.0098)	(.0374)	—	—	—
(4)	.4919	—	—	.2250	.3039	.4568	.9557	.6776	.4974
	—	—	—	(.0457)	(.0491)	(.0648)	—	—	—
California Major Irrigation Counties [2]									
(1)	2.0592	.0911	−.1132	.3882	.0085	.4933	.8680	.9296	.1859
	—	(.1158)	(.0780)	(.0759)	(.0105)	(.0832)	—	—	—
(2)	1.7886	.0968	—	.3485	.0093	.4521	.9067	.9218	.1910
	—	(.1189)	—	(.0726)	(.0190)	(.0803)	—	—	—
(4)	1.7368	—	—	.3833	.0138	.5059	.9031	.9192	.1894
	—	—	—	(.0583)	(.0180)	(.0452)	—	—	—
(5)	2.0641	—	—	.3710	—	.5021	.8731	.9169	.1876
	—	—	—	(.0556)	—	(.0445)	—	—	—

TABLE A1.6—Continued

California Limited Irrigation Counties [3]									
(1)	.6873	.2465	.0171	.1431	.1456	.4871	1.0394	.9375	.3269
	—	(.1410)	(.1606)	(.0771)	(.0732)	(.1270)	—	—	—
(2)	.7581	.2404	—	.1467	.1486	.4954	1.0311	.9374	.3191
	—	(.1258)	—	(.0678)	(.0660)	(.0976)	—	—	—
(4)	.7127	—	—	.1984	.1852	.6413	1.0249	.9266	.3304
	—	—	—	(.0643)	(.0654)	(.0628)	—	—	—
California—All Counties									
(1)	.3241	.2620	.1735	.2667	.0279	.3813	1.1114	.9724	.2594
	—	(.0896)	(.0895)	(.0347)	(.0206)	(.0699)	—	—	—
(2)	—	.2648	—	.2200	.0360	.5017	1.0225	.9119	.2886
	—	(.0990)	—	(.0481)	(.0227)	(.0699)	—	—	—
(4)	.8909	—	—	.3335	.0538	.6426	1.0299	.9613	.3034
	—	—	—	(.0357)	(.0227)	(.0370)	—	—	—

[1] Irrigation counties are defined to include all counties with 1,000 acres or more of irrigated cropland in 1954.

[2] In California, major irrigation counties include the 25 counties in Southern California and the Sacramento and San Joaquin valleys in which 50,000 acres or more of irrigated cropland were harvested in 1954.

[3] In California the limited irrigation counties include the counties with less than 50,000 acres of irrigated cropland in 1954 plus Siskiyou County in northern California. San Francisco County is omitted because of the limited amount of agriculture in the county. In addition, Placer and El Dorado; Alpine, Amador, and Calaveras; Tuolumne and Mariposa; Del Norte and Humboldt; and Mono and Inyo counties were grouped because of the low value of farm output in these counties.

TABLE A1.7. Alternative Resource Productivity Coefficients for Irrigation Counties[1] in Mountain Type-of-Farming Regions, 1954

Region and equation	Constant term (in $\log_e$) a_0	All farm workers X_1	Livestock investment X_3	Irrigated cropland X_4	Non-irrigated cropland X_5	Current operating expense X_6	Sum of coefficients	Coefficient of determination R^2	Standard error of estimate (in $\log_e$) $\overline{S}$
Northern Mountain									
(1)	.5093	.7077	.3271	.0430	.1018	−.0116	1.1681	.8224	.3512
	—	(.0872)	(.0662)	(.0378)	(.0254)	(.0771)	—	—	—
(2)	.8782	.6758	—	.0924	.1404	.1237	1.0324	.7819	.4927
	—	(.0296)	—	(.0223)	(.0047)	(.0420)	—	—	—
(4)	.8074	—	—	.1608	.2397	.5514	.9519	.6816	.4659
	—	—	—	(.0469)	(.0272)	(.0617)	—	—	—
Southern Mountain									
(1)	.7567	.5317	.2097	.1056	.0075	.2834	1.1378	.8939	.4331
	—	(.0546)	(.0789)	(.0420)	(.0159)	(.0584)	—	—	—
(2)	1.0235	.5369	—	.1288	.0154	.3596	1.0407	.8884	.4425
	—	(.0159)	—	(.0090)	(.0013)	(.0138)	—	—	—
(4)	.9379	—	—	.2554	.0200	.6953	.9707	.8135	.5701
	—	—	—	(.0514)	(.0205)	(.0498)	—	—	—

[1] Includes counties with 1,000 acres or more of irrigated cropland harvested in 1954.

TABLE A1.8. Alternative Resource Productivity Coefficients for Major and Limited Irrigation Counties[1] in the Southern Plains Type-of-Farming Region, 1954

Region and equation	Constant term (in $\log_e$) a_0	All farm workers X_1	Livestock investment X_3	Irrigated cropland X_4	Non-irrigated cropland X_5	Current operating expense X_6	Sum of coefficients	Coefficient of determination R^2	Standard error of estimate (in $\log_e$) $\overline{S}$
All irrigation counties									
(1)	.6254	.2912	.1971	.2033	.1232	.1786	.9934	.7936	.4065
		(.0356)	(.0720)	(.0101)	(.0150)	(.0552)	—	—	—
(2)	.8779	.2726	—	.2049	.1311	.2881	.8967	.7886	.4107
		(.0076)	—	(.0062)	(.0013)	(.0087)	—	—	—
(4)	.9112	—	—	.2228	.1855	.4550	.8633	.7475	.4481
		—	—	(.0109)	(.0142)	(.0346)	—	—	—
Major irrigation counties									
(1)	.4922	.3349	.1048	.2932	.1157	.1546	1.0032	.8020	.3197
		(.0441)	(.0800)	(.0199)	(.0146)	(.0650)	—	—	—
(2)	.6640	.3157	—	.2890	.1162	.2193	.9402	.8000	.3203
		(.0169)	—	(.0038)	(.0021)	(.0174)	—	—	—
(4)	.7388	—	—	.3488	.1432	.3894	.8814	.7330	.3690
		—	—	(.0207)	(.0163)	(.0412)	—	—	—
Limited irrigation counties									
(1)	−.1077	.0993	.6159	.1059	.1729	.1172	1.1112	.8013	.4219
		(.0580)	(.1223)	(.0258)	(.0295)	(.0813)	—	—	—
(2)	.6034	.0805	—	.1230	.2124	.4061	.8220	.7626	.4594
		(.0188)	—	(.0037)	(.0045)	(.0188)	—	—	—
(4)	.5568	—	—	.1194	.2395	.4482	.8071	.7330	.3690
				(.0277)	(.0225)	(.0535)	—	—	—

[1] Major irrigation counties are defined to include counties with 1,000 acres or more of irrigated cropland harvested in 1954. Limited irrigation counties include counties with between 10 and 999 acres of irrigated cropland harvested in 1954.

TABLE A1.9. Alternative Resource Productivity Coefficients for Irrigation Counties[1] in the Northern Plains Type-of-Farming Region, 1954

Region and equation	Constant term (in $\log_e$) a_0	All farm workers X_1	Livestock investment X_3	Irrigated cropland X_4	Non-irrigated cropland X_5	Current operating expense X_6	Sum of coefficients	Coefficient of determination R^2	Standard error of estimate (in $\log_e$) $\bar{S}$
All irrigation counties									
(1)	.0201	.2300	−.0285	.0404	.3680	.3422	.9521	.8579	.2376
		(.0448)	(.0408)	(.0070)	(.0369)	(.0246)	—	—	—
(2)	.0081	.2265	—	.0408	.3614	.3362	.9649	.8576	.2369
		(.0350)	—	(.0009)	(.0226)	(.0094)	—	—	—
(4)	−.5261	—	—	.0367	.4891	.4268	.9526	.8435	.2485
		—	—	(.0072)	(.0265)	(.0153)	—	—	—
Major irrigation counties									
(1)	.2252	.3890	−.1122	.0763	.3233	.3062	.9826	.8662	.2225
		(.0813)	(.0575)	(.0175)	(.0496)	(.0466)	—	—	—
(2)	.0939	.3394	—	.0756	.3177	.2790	1.0117	.8571	.2254
		(.1206)	—	(.0062)	(.0494)	(.0400)	—	—	—
(4)	−.2911	—	—	.0795	.4276	.4418	.9488	.8316	.2436
		—	—	(.0191)	(.0467)	(.0270)	—	—	—
Limited irrigation counties									
(1)	−.3754	.1291	−.0250	.0322	.4531	.3768	.9662	.8652	.2422
		(.0603)	(.0700)	(.0169)	(.0601)	(.0326)	—	—	—
(2)	−.3646	.1325	—	.0319	.4423	.3714	.8781	.8651	.2407
		(.0035)	—	(.0003)	(.0027)	(.0082)	—	—	—
(4)	−.7750	—	—	.0248	.5338	.4212	.9799	.8606	.2446
			—	(.0167)	(.0222)	(.0184)	—	—	—

[1] Major irrigation counties are defined to include counties with 1,000 acres or more of irrigated cropland harvested in 1954. Limited irrigation counties include counties with between 10 and 999 acres of irrigated cropland harvested in 1954.

TABLE A1.10. Alternative Resource Productivity Coefficients for Irrigation Counties[1] in Northern Type-of-Farming Regions, 1954

Region and equation	Constant term (in $\log_e$) a_0	All farm workers X_1	Machinery investment X_2	Irrigated cropland X_4	Non-irrigated cropland X_5	Current operating expense X_6	Sum of coefficients	Coefficient of determination R^2	Standard error of estimate (in $\log_e$) $\overline{S}$
Northeast									
(1)	1.8840	.4098	.0618	.0909	−.0563	.3934	.8996	.9068	.2660
		(.0761)	(.0895)	(.0143)	(.0414)	(.0342)	—	—	—
(2)	1.6836	.4472	—	.0921	−.0340	.3977	.9030	.9066	.2958
		(.0404)	—	(.0028)	(.0092)	(.0164)	—	—	—
(3)	2.4158	—	.3998	.0990	−.1165	.4336	.8159	.8938	.2875
		—	(.0550)	(.0028)	(.0217)	(.0152)	—	—	—
(4)	2.2369	—	—	.1249	.1007	.5813	.8067	.8754	.3105
		—	—	(.0026)	(.0055)	(.0096)	—	—	—
Lake States									
(1)	.8731	−.0464	.4450	.0288	.2522	.2846	1.0644	.9088	.2839
		(.1257)	(.1619)	(.0217)	(.0828)	(.0682)	—	—	—
(2)	.4965	.2086	—	.0137	.3754	.4781	1.0759	.9041	.2694
		(.0852)	—	(.0052)	(.0578)	(.0417)	—	—	—
(3)	.8147	—	.4007	.0249	.2560	.3874	1.0692	.9087	.2888
		—	(.1087)	(.0191)	(.0819)	(.0676)	—	—	—
(4)	1.9855	—	—	.0365	.4590	.5417	1.0372	.9004	.3066
		—	—	(.0042)	(.0412)	(.0338)	—	—	—
Corn Belt									
(1)	.2047	−.2134	.9153	.0313	.3327	.1866	1.2526	.8901	.2464
		(.0601)	(.0577)	(.0132)	(.0474)	(.0445)	—	—	—
(2)	−.9026	.3113	—	.0186	.6056	.4317	1.3673	.7833	.3493
		(.0427)	—	(.0118)	(.0192)	(.0426)	—	—	—
(3)	−.1658	—	.8094	.0147	.3204	.1860	1.3305	.8851	.2543
		—	(.0491)	(.0125)	(.0492)	(.0454)	—	—	—
(4)	−.4083	—	—	.0496	.6950	.4908	1.2354	.7684	.3604
		—	—	(.0024)	(.0295)	(.0265)	—	—	—

[1] Irrigation counties are defined to include all counties with 10 acres or more of irrigated cropland harvested or pastured in 1954.

TABLE A1.11. Alternative Resource Productivity Coefficients for Irrigation Counties[1] in Southern Type-of-Farming Regions, 1954

Region and equation	Constant term (in $\log_e$) a_0	All farm workers X_1	Machinery investment X_2	Irrigated cropland X_4	Non-irrigated cropland X_5	Current operating expense X_6	Sum of coefficients	Coefficient of determination R^2	Standard error of estimate (in $\log_e$) $\bar{S}$
Appalachian									
(1)	.4734	.3765	.2504	.0437	.1631	.3536	1.1873	.8422	.3350
	—	(.0427)	(.0570)	(.0171)	(.0457)	(.0446)	—	—	—
(4)	.5152	—	—	.0736	.4661	.6303	1.1700	.7875	.3911
	—	—	—	(.0024)	(.0096)	(.0092)	—	—	—
Southeast									
(1)	.6911	.1890	.1674	.0435	.2214	.4645	1.0856	.8562	.2766
	—	(.0427)	(.0570)	(.0171)	(.0457)	(.0446)	—	—	—
(4)	.6553	—	—	.0668	.4154	.5652	1.0474	.8348	.2993
	—	—	—	(.0036)	(.0111)	(.0144)	—	—	—
Florida									
(1)	1.4742	.1201	.1049	.1947	.0932	.6045	1.1200	.9471	.2937
	—	(.1224)	(.1233)	(.0264)	(.0464)	(.0801)	—	—	—
(4)	1.1407	—	—	.1999	.1600	.7364	1.0963	.9415	.3199
	—	—	—	(.0073)	(.0169)	(.0428)	—	—	—
Delta									
(1)	.9245	.5638	.0824	.1463	.0228	.2226	1.0380	.8743	.3475
	—	(.0588)	(.0533)	(.0146)	(.0807)	(.0501)	—	—	—
(4)	.5379	—	—	.1663	.6028	.2930	1.0621	.7998	.4432
	—	—	—	(.0015)	(.0251)	(.0194)	—	—	—

[1] Irrigation counties are defined to include all counties with 10 acres or more of irrigated cropland harvested or pastured in 1954.

TABLE A1.12. Alternative Factor Marginal Value Productivity Estimates for Major Irrigation Counties in the Water Resource Regions, 1954

Water resource region and equation[1]		All farm workers		Irrigated land		Nonirrigated cropland		Current operating expense	
		Geometric mean	Arithmetic mean	Geometric mean	Arithmetic mean	Geometric mean	Arithmetic mean	Geometric mean	Arithmetic mean
		($/year)		($/acre)		($/acre)		($/$)	
Pacific									
Pacific Northwest	(1)	1,051.22	1,080.88	77.39	63.32	60.93	35.97	2.60	2.12
	(2)	1,353.51	1,391.70	77.06	63.04	62.81	37.07	2.62	2.14
	(3)	1,350.91	1,389.03	75.15	61.48	62.45	36.86	2.58	2.11
Central Pacific	(1)	1,448.78	1,648.48	60.26	54.88	98.34	131.00	2.95	2.79
	(2)	1,648.51	1,875.74	70.74	64.42	99.04	131.94	3.08	2.92
	(3)	1,761.11	2,003.86	63.80	58.10	92.25	122.89	2.68	2.53
	(F2)	—	—	78.75	91.14	11.02	14.68	3.32	3.14
South Pacific[2]	(1)	1,752.52	1,694.94	*	*	n	n	2.36	2.02
	(2)	2,031.83	1,965.07	75.56	76.42	n	n	2.48	2.12
	(3)	2,088.21	2,019.61	84.37	85.32	n	n	2.66	2.28
	(6)	*	*	395.40	399.89	—	—	*	*
	(7)	—	—	413.47	418.16	—	—	1.34	1.10
Southern Mountain									
Colorado River	(1)	947.11	142.21	*	*	n	n	3.97	3.73
	(2)	1,018.74	152.96	11.04	17.13	n	n	4.07	3.82
	(3)	1,012.30	152.00	12.04	18.68	*	*	5.48	5.14
Great Basin	(1)	*	*	*	*	*	*	*	*
	(2)	1,414.85	1,209.42	*	*	*	*	1.63	1.37
	(3)	1,077.85	921.34	29.18	30.84	*	*	2.34	1.97
Upper Rio Grande and Pecos	(1)	685.93	685.02	81.31	79.12	n	n	3.75	3.82
	(2)	684.05	683.14	65.19	63.43	n	n	3.45	3.51
	(3)	716.67	715.71	61.87	60.21	n	n	3.96	4.03
Great Plains									
Upper Missouri	(1)	904.16	778.18	28.10	21.49	4.88	3.04	1.67	1.33
	(2)	2,655.36	2,285.39	76.99	58.87	9.74	6.06	.92	.74
	(3)	2,815.51	2,423.23	85.53	65.41	7.79	6.09	.94	.75
Upper Arkansas-White-Red	(1)	407.72	297.60	86.16	83.58	13.79	11.86	3.21	2.09
	(2)	747.74	545.78	92.33	89.58	16.09	13.84	4.15	2.69
	(3)	818.35	597.32	91.72	88.99	15.70	13.50	3.35	2.18
Western Gulf	(1)	143.75	112.44	157.46	92.86	23.32	13.74	1.51	.99
	(2)	365.30	285.74	190.89	112.58	40.85	24.06	2.72	1.78
	(3)	367.17	287.20	191.01	112.65	40.88	24.08	2.69	1.76

(*See notes at end of table.*)

TABLE A1.12.—Continued.

Water resource region and equation[1]		All farm workers		Irrigated land		Nonirrigated cropland		Current operating expense	
		Geometric mean	Arithmetic mean	Geometric mean	Arithmetic mean	Geometric mean	Arithmetic mean	Geometric mean	Arithmetic mean
		($/year)		($/acre)		($/acre)		($/$)	
North									
Northeast	(1)	*	*	727.31	1,036.82	n	n	1.47	1.35
	(2)	1,305.52	1,171.83	773.62	1,102.84	*	*	1.49	1.37
	(3)	1,162.88	1,043.80	902.06	1,285.94	*	*	1.40	1.28
Great Lakes	(1)	*	*	*	*	*	*	*	*
	(2)	873.11	995.93	*	*	30.62	21.32	1.58	1.23
	(3)	833.61	950.88	*	*	*	*	*	*
	(F1)	n	n	658.13	1,013.22	22.76	15.85	1.53	1.19
Corn Belt	(1)	*	*	*	*	*	*	2.10	1.97
	(2)	*	*	*	*	*	*	3.17	2.98
	(3)	*	*	*	*	*	*	3.14	2.95
	(F1)			303.75	2,840.75	20.99	20.80	.96	.90
South									
Southeast	(1)	528.39	463.39	*	*	13.44	12.09	1.95	1.71
	(2)	621.19	544.77	*	*	15.72	14.14	2.27	1.99
	(3)	622.86	546.24	*	*	*	*	2.02	1.77
	(F1)	261.32	229.17	335.57	806.77	15.96	14.35	2.03	1.78
Florida	(1)	*	*	325.23	312.77	38.85	24.58	2.80	2.86
	(2)	598.87	559.82	327.76	315.21	39.18	24.78	2.81	2.88
	(3)	615.83	575.68	315.34	303.26	33.91	21.45	2.73	2.80
Lower Mississippi	(1)	252.20	218.65	254.64	169.73	70.41	63.30	*	*
	(2)	251.86	218.34	250.16	166.75	89.68	62.64	*	*
	(3)	205.94	178.54	332.34	221.52	74.23	66.73	n	n
Lower Arkansas-White-Red	(1)	579.52	609.46	333.11	243.69	*	*	2.13	1.41
	(2)	590.86	621.39	352.85	258.13	*	*	2.23	1.48
	(3)	610.46	642.00	334.09	244.41	*	*	2.32	1.53

* Indicates that the coefficient for this variable was rejected because it was small relative to its standard error.

n Indicates that the coefficient for this variable was rejected because it was negative.

— Indicates that no coefficient for this variable was computed.

[1] Equation numbers preceded by "F" refer to type-of-farming regions.

[2] Equations (1), (2), and (3) for the South Pacific are based on the coefficients estimated for the combined South Pacific and Colorado River regions. Equations (6) and (7) are based on the coefficients calculated for the seven South Pacific counties alone.

TABLE A1.13. Factor Marginal Productivity Estimates in Humid and Arid Type-of-Farming Region Areas, 1954

Region and area	Equation	All farm workers X_1	Machinery investment X_2	Irrigated cropland X_4	Non-irrigated cropland X_5	Current operating expenses X_6
		($/year)	($/tractor)	($/acre)	($/acre)	($/$ spent)
		Calculated at geometric means				
North						
Northeast	(2)	1,181		3,314	−4.51	1.18
Lake States	(2)	449		774	20.71	2.54
Corn Belt	(2)	905		1,403	35.35	1.75
South						
Appalachian	(1)	475	1,115	1,237	10.50	1.53
Southeast	(1)	240	809	941	12.69	1.58
Florida	(1)	396	1,040	515	17.64	2.36
Delta	(1)	595	373	714	1.29	1.04
Plains						
Northern						
All irrigation counties	(2)	930		373	12.32	3.15
Major irrigation counties	(2)	1,555		91	11.93	2.66
Limited irrigation counties	(2)	504		1,198	14.10	3.43
Southern						
All irrigation counties	(2)	580		1,018	13.15	1.59
Major irrigation counties	(2)	988		211	16.53	2.21
Limited irrigation counties	(2)	133		2,103	17.03	1.53
Mountain						
Northern	(2)	2,934		21	26.85	1.47
Southern	(2)	1,620		25	21.39	2.38
Pacific						
Northwest	(2)	1,681		170	62.12	1.62
California						
All irrigation counties	(2)	1,206		104	32.67	3.43
Major irrigation counties	(4)			146		3.70
Limited irrigation counties	(2)	888		98	67.72	3.02
		Calculated at arithmetic means				
North						
Northeast	(2)	1,117		1,130	−3.91	1.13
Lake States	(2)	508		428	21.66	2.48
Corn Belt	(2)	1,051		801	38.88	1.88
South						
Appalachian	(1)	551	1,266	884	12.38	1.46
Southeast	(1)	238	838	608	12.62	1.53
Florida	(1)	527	1,449	213	19.06	2.83
Delta	(1)	655	490	103	1.62	1.24
Plains						
Northern						
All irrigation counties	(2)	879		66	11.59	2.47
Major irrigation counties	(2)	1,554		46	12.24	2.13
Limited irrigation counties	(2)	472		1,003	12.92	2.68
Southern						
All irrigation counties	(2)	588		91	8.81	1.75
Major irrigation counties	(2)	971		77	10.00	2.21
Limited irrigation counties	(2)	122		1,072	10.87	1.58
Mountain						
Northern	(2)	3,025		17	11.72	1.38
Southern	(2)	1,999		29	3.60	2.36
Pacific						
Northwest	(2)	1,640		98	44.64	1.58
California						
All irrigation counties	(2)	1,379		83	34.17	2.92
Major irrigation counties	(4)			134		3.10
Limited irrigation counties	(2)	861		87	50.01	2.05

APPENDIX 2.

Total and Average Farm Output and Input Measures for Water Resource Regions

TABLE A2.1. Total and Average Farm Output and Input Measures for Counties in the Mountain and Pacific Water Resource Regions, 1954

Region	Counties	Farm sales	All farm workers	Irrigated land [1]	Non-irrigated cropland	Operating expenses
	(number)	(million $)	(thousand persons)	(thousand acres)	(thousand acres)	(million $)
A. *Total*						
Pacific Northwest						
Major irrigation counties [2]	106	1,123.3	309.8	4,340.9	4,710.7	143.2
All counties	125	1,173.4	326.0	4,353.2	7,776.8	165.3
Central Pacific [3]						
Major irrigation counties [2]	42	1,574.1	332.7	5,966.2	2,040.4	222.6
All counties	43	1,585.9	333.8	6,063.7	2,052.2	228.6
South Pacific						
Major irrigation counties [2]	7	579.4	89.5	789.4	369.3	145.4
Colorado River						
Major irrigation counties [2,4]	50	526.4	109.9	2,802.5	271.5	59.6
All counties	52	533.8	112.3	2,813.3	395.2	60.4
Great Basin [5]						
Major irrigation counties [2]	39	170.2	53.3	1,922.8	342.4	29.7
All counties	41	170.4	53.4	1,935.7	671.6	29.8
Upper Rio Grande and Pecos						
Major irrigation counties [2]	38	224.1	104.5	1,130.4	393.8	28.3
All counties	46	232.7	106.3	1,132.2	396.5	31.6
	(number)	(thousand $)	(persons)	(acres)	(acres)	(thousand $)
B. *Average (arithmetic)*						
Pacific Northwest						
Major irrigation counties [2]	106	10,597	2,923	40,952	44,441	1,351
All counties	125	9,387	2,608	34,824	62,214	1,323
Central Pacific [3]						
Major irrigation counties [2]	42	37,478	7,922	142,051	48,580	5,300
All counties	43	36,880	7,763	141,016	47,726	5,316

TABLE A2.1.—Continued.

Region	Counties	Farm sales	All farm workers	Irrigated land [1]	Non-irrigated cropland	Operating expenses
	(number)	(thousand $)	(persons)	(acres)	(acres)	(thousand $)
South Pacific						
Major irrigation counties [2]	7	82,771	12,785	112,786	—	20,771
Colorado River						
Major irrigation counties [2]	49	10,743	2,242	57,194	5,541	1,216
All counties	52	10,265	2,160	54,201	7,600	1,162
Great Basin [5]						
Major irrigation counties [2]	39	4,364	1,368	49,303	8,779	763
All counties	41	4,155	1,303	47,212	16,380	728
Upper Rio Grande and Pecos						
Major irrigation counties [2]	38	5,897	2,749	29,748	10,364	744
All counties	46	5,058	2,311	24,613	8,600	686
C. *Average (geometric)*						
Pacific Northwest						
Major irrigation counties [2]	106	6,700	1,914	20,336	26,205	770
Central Pacific [3]						
Major irrigation counties [2]	42	17,169	4,112	59,785	29,597	2,338
South Pacific						
Major irrigation counties [2]	7	76,345	11,405	105,355	—	16,465
Colorado River						
Major irrigation counties [2,4]	49	2,925	924	23,955	532	311
Great Basin [5]						
Major irrigation counties [2]	39	2,951	791	35,445	883	433
Upper Rio Grande and Pecos						
Major irrigation counties [2]	38	3,313	1,512	15,689	1,090	458

[1] Including both irrigated cropland and pasture.

[2] Major irrigation counties are defined to include only counties with 1,000 or more acres of irrigated cropland.

[3] In the Central Pacific Region the following counties were combined and treated as single counties: (1) Placer and El Dorado, (2) Alpine, Amador, and Calaveras, (3) Tuolumne and Mariposa, and (4) Del Norte and Humboldt.

[4] Hildalgo County, New Mexico, was not included among the major irrigation counties even though it meets the major county definition.

[5] In the Great Basin, Mono and Inyo counties were combined and treated as a single county.

TABLE A2.2. Total and Average Farm Output and Input Measures for Counties in the Great Plains Water Resource Regions

Region	Counties	Farm sales	All farm workers	Irrigated land [1]	Non-irrigated cropland	Operating expenses
	(number)	(million $)	(thousand persons)	(thousand acres)	(thousand acres)	(million $)
A. *Total*						
Upper Missouri River						
Major irrigation counties [2]	160	1,351.3	272.5	4,525.2	26,536.2	178.3
All counties	361	2,964.0	729.3	4,621.7	80,890.2	389.9
Upper Arkansas-White-Red						
Major irrigation counties [2]	81	521.5	140.0	1,381.6	13,755.8	54.5
All counties	153	948.3	310.5	1,409.4	24,087.3	134.5
Western Gulf						
Major irrigation counties [2]	75	873.4	269.4	3,775.9	7,331.2	86.8
All counties	199	1,406.6	625.7	4,431.5	16,176.5	221.6
	(number)	(thousand $)	(persons)	(acres)	(acres)	(thousand $)
B. *Average (arithmetic)*						
Upper Missouri River						
Major irrigation counties [2]	160	8,446	1,703	28,283	165,851	1,114
All counties	361	8,211	2,020	12,803	224,073	1,080
Upper Arkansas-White-Red						
Major irrigation counties [2]	81	6,327	1,728	17,057	169,825	673
All counties	153	6,198	2,029	9,212	157,433	879
Western Gulf						
Major irrigation counties [2]	75	11,645	3,592	50,345	97,749	1,157
All counties	199	7,068	3,144	22,269	81,289	1,114
C. *Average (geometric)*						
Upper Missouri River						
Major irrigation counties [2]	154	6,928	1,467	8,266	117,721	728
Upper Arkansas-White-Red						
Major irrigation counties [2]	81	5,064	1,210	7,302	110,588	467
Western Gulf						
Major irrigation counties [2]	75	7,709	2,682	14,323	52,233	793

[1] Including both irrigated cropland and pasture.

[2] Major irrigation counties are defined to include only counties with 1,000 acres or more of irrigated cropland in 1954.

TABLE A2.3. Total and Average Farm Output and Input Measures for Counties in Northern Water Resource Regions

Region	Counties	Farm sales	All farm workers	Irrigated land [1]	Non-irrigated cropland	Operating expenses
	(number)	(million $)	(thousand persons)	(thousand acres)	(thousand acres)	(million $)
A. *Total*						
Northeast						
Major irrigation counties [2]	59	929.9	294.4	163.9	4,989.3	356.0
Limited irrigation counties [3]	153	992.9	410.6	24.4	9,578.9	379.0
All counties	260	2,056.0	753.9	188.7	15,874.5	776.7
Great Lakes						
Major irrigation counties [2]	25	362.0	166.7	31.8	3,992.3	70.9
Limited irrigation counties [3]	129	1,237.6	456.4	19.0	18,687.6	268.8
All counties	194	1,788.2	698.2	50.8	28,461.9	426.8
Corn Belt						
Major irrigation counties [2]	35	326.0	120.7	36.1	5,115.4	68.2
Limited irrigation counties [3]	340	3,185.8	1,084.2	40.3	53,247.2	738.3
All counties	711	6,892.7	2,141.6	77.6	112,499.0	1,452.6
	(number)	(thousand $)	(persons)	(acres)	(acres)	(thousand $)
B. *Average (arithmetic)*						
Northeast						
Major irrigation counties [2]	59	15,761.3	4,820	2,777	84,564	6,034.6
Limited irrigation counties [3]	153	11,156.5	4,614	275	107,628	4,258.4
All counties	260	7,907.7	2,899	725	61,100	2,987.3
Great Lakes						
Major irrigation counties [2]	25	14,481.6	6,669	1,271	159,690	2,836.3
Limited irrigation counties [3]	129	15,866.2	5,852	243	239,585	3,445.5
All counties	194	9,217.5	3,599	262	146,711	2,200.0
Corn Belt						
Major irrigation counties [2]	35	9,315.7	3,448	1,030	146,154	1,948.3
Limited irrigation counties [3]	340	9,370.0	3,189	119	156,609	2,171.5
All counties	711	9,892.7	3,012	109	158,200	2,043.0
C. *Average (geometric)*						
Northeast						
Major irrigation counties [2]	59	11,865.9	3,906	1,553	53,993	4,107.8
Limited irrigation counties [3]	153	4,517.3	1,933	100	39,657	1,526.8
Great Lakes						
Major irrigation counties [2]	25	13,494.2	6,010	1,050	149,513	2,506.1
Limited irrigation counties [3]	129	7,143.7	3,051	102	116,210	1,479.4

(*See notes at end of table.*)

TABLE A2.3.—Continued

Region	Counties	Farm sales	All farm workers	Irrigated land [1]	Non-irrigated cropland	Operating expenses
	(number)	(thousand $)	(persons)	(acres)	(acres)	(thousand $)
Corn Belt						
Major irrigation counties [2]	35	8,219.8	3,166	847	130,276	1,596.4
Limited irrigation counties [3]	340	6,875.3	2,872	75	124,651	1,648.2

[1] Includes both irrigated cropland and pasture.
[2] Major irrigation counties are defined to include counties with 500 or more acres of irrigated cropland in 1954.
[3] Limited irrigation counties are defined to include counties with between 10 and 499 acres of irrigated cropland in 1954.

TABLE A2.4. Measures of Total and Average Farm Output and Input Measures for Counties in Southern Water Resource Regions

Region	Counties	Farm sales	All farm workers	Irrigated land [1]	Non-irrigated cropland	Operating expenses
	(number)	(million $)	(thousand persons)	(thousand acres)	(thousand acres)	(million $)
A. *Total*						
Southeast						
Major irrigation counties [2]	70	508.0	371.1	67.2	6,809.4	109.1
Limited irrigation counties [3]	40	1,533.3	1,276.5	55.5	23,100.9	412.4
All counties	536	2,286.4	1,885.9	123.0	35,257.2	597.3
Florida						
Major irrigation counties [2]	41	423.2	83.0	427.1	1,603.9	84.9
Limited irrigation counties [3]	19	38.9	22.2	2.4	657.4	13.7
All counties	67	466.1	108.9	[4] 429.5	2,385.3	100.1
Lower Mississippi						
Major irrigation counties [2]	52	703.6	565.1	528.7	8,169.4	60.4
Limited irrigation counties [3]	44	179.0	202.7	7.2	3,382.9	32.2
All counties	108	903.8	800.7	535.9	12,241.6	98.8
Lower Arkansas-White-Red						
Major irrigation counties [2]	43	304.9	241.2	570.7	4,823.3	67.8
Limited irrigation counties [3]	51	114.0	112.2	9.5	3,408.4	58.1
All counties	155	650.5	521.0	597.9	12,798.5	193.7

TABLE A2.4.—Continued.

Region	Counties	Farm sales	All farm workers	Irrigated land [1]	Non-irrigated cropland	Operating expenses
	(number)	(thousand $)	(persons)	(acres)	(acres)	(thousand $)
B. *Average (arithmetic)*						
Southeast						
Major irrigation counties [2]	70	7,257	5,302	961	97,277	1,559
Limited irrigation counties [3]	40	5,700	4,745	206	85,877	1,533
All counties	536	4,266	3,518	230	65,800	1,114
Florida						
Major irrigation counties [2]	41	10,321	2,023	10,416	39,120	2,071
Limited irrigation counties [3]	19	2,050	1,167	126	34,601	724
All counties	67	6,957	1,626	6,385	35,600	1,494
Lower Mississippi						
Major irrigation counties [2]	52	13,531	10,867	10,167	157,104	1,162
Limited irrigation counties [3]	44	4,069	4,607	164	76,883	732
All counties	108	8,368	7,414	4,962	113,300	916
Lower Arkansas-White-Red						
Major irrigation counties [2]	43	7,090	5,609	13,272	112,170	1,578
Limited irrigation counties [3]	51	2,234	2,200	186	66,832	1,139
All counties	155	4,197	3,361	3,857	82,600	1,250
C. *Average (geometric)*						
Southeast						
Major irrigation counties [2]	70	5,825	4,213	842	80,829	1,333
Limited irrigation counties [3]	40	6,875	2,872	75	124,651	1,648
Florida						
Major irrigation counties [2]	41	6,211	1,357	5,482	20,106	1,364
Limited irrigation counties	19	1,259	776	80	19,138	452
Lower Mississippi						
Major irrigation counties [2]	52	10,707	8,224	4,232	130,313	990
Limited irrigation counties [3]	44	3,115	3,124	106	54,513	567
Lower Arkansas-White-Red						
Major irrigation counties [2]	43	5,657	4,764	3,803	103,430	1,116
Limited irrigation counties [3]	51	1,717	1,982	143	56,606	871

[1] Includes both irrigated cropland and pasture.

[2] Major irrigation counties are defined to include counties with 500 or more acres of irrigated cropland in 1954.

[3] Limited irrigation counties are defined to include counties with between 10 and 499 acres of irrigated cropland in 1954.

[4] The sum of the individual county figures exceeds the state total presented in *U.S. Census of Agriculture, 1954.*

APPENDIX 3.

National and Regional Farm Output Projections

Attempts to project the output possibilities and requirements of U.S. agriculture have become increasingly frequent during the last decade and a half.

The projections made prior to 1955, particularly those of the Cooke and Paley Commissions for 1975, the short-run projections of the Land Grant Colleges–Department of Agriculture Joint Committee on Agricultural Productive Capacity, and the projections by Cochrane and Lampe[1] were centered mainly around the question of agriculture's ability to meet the requirements stemming from an expanding population and the possible necessity of facing periods of alternating hot and cold wars. The concern with the effects of population growth was related to a growing realization that the nation was in the midst of a baby boom and that the population projections of the 1930's and 1940's were far below the levels that would actually obtain in the last half of the century.

Since the mid-1950's, this concern has been almost reversed. By and large the concern was no longer one of whether farm output could be expected to expand rapidly enough to meet the new demands being placed upon it. Projection studies began to focus on two other questions: Would even the rapid growth of population being projected for the 1960's and 1970's be sufficient to reduce the pressure of rapidly expanding farm output on prices received by farmers? In the event that technological change continued to outrun population growth, what types of adjustments in resource inputs would be required?

[1] See Table A3.1 for references. For an annotated bibliography of some recent agricultural projection studies see A. L. Barr, *Studies of Agricultural Production Projections,* U.S. Department of Agriculture, Agricultural Research Service (Washington, February, 1961).

NATIONAL FARM OUTPUT PROJECTIONS

The results of several of the long-run output projections for U.S. agriculture that have been made since 1950 are summarized in Table A3.1. The projections fall fairly neatly into two groups. The ones made before 1955 adopted the medium population projections of the Bureau of the Census in *Current Population Reports P–25,* No. 78 (August, 1953) or earlier official or semiofficial projections, while those made since 1955 have typically adopted the highest population projections of P-25, No. 78, or projections from subsequent Bureau of the Census releases—P-25, No. 123 (October 20, 1955) and P-25, No. 187 (November 10, 1958).

The characteristics of these postwar projections deserve additional comment. First, there is relatively close agreement between projections based on the same or similar population estimates. This is not surprising in view of the projection techniques employed. The procedure has usually been to assume a population elasticity of demand of exactly 1.0, an average income elasticity of demand for food products of between 0.15 and 0.25, and an average income elasticity of demand for nonfood farm products in the neighborhood of zero. In some cases the aggregate projections have been built up from estimates of the demand for individual commodities. In other cases, the average elasticities have been applied directly to the food and nonfood aggregates. There has been considerable variation in the per capita income assumptions employed, but variations in the income projection and in aggregation procedures have had relatively little effect on the final projections. Population growth has tended to dwarf the impact of aggregation procedures and income growth.

Second, although almost all of the projections represent to some extent "variations on a theme by Daly," the "unofficial" projections made during any given year tend to be higher than Daly's "official" U.S. Department of Agriculture projections. The "unofficial" projectors have generally felt free to adopt higher population estimates earlier than Daly. The population assumptions made in the "official" and "unofficial" estimates showed closer agreement during the late 1950's. This appears to reflect an attitude on the part of those constructing "unofficial" pro-

TABLE A3.1. A Comparison of Output Projections for United States Agriculture

Source	Date published or reported	Base period	Original projections: Population assumption (in millions)	Original projections: Projected output index (base period = 100)	Adjusted output projections: 1947–49 = 100	Adjusted output projections: 1955 = 100
Projections to 1955:						
Joint Committee on Productive Capacity * [1]	1952	1950	n.a.	120	121	107
Projections to 1960:						
Cooke Commission [2]	1950	1945–49	169	117	119	105
Ruttan [3]	1956	1950	177	122	123	109
Projections to 1965:						
Cochrane and Lampe † [4]	1953	1935–39	176	152–161	116–122	103–108
Black and Bonnen [5]	1956	1955	190	113–117	128–132	113–117
Daly [6]	1957	1956	115	114–119	130–134	115–120
Daly and Barton [6]	1958	1947–49	115	130	131	122
Collins and Mehren † [7]	1958	1955	190–193	120–121	134–136	120–121
Projections to 1970:						
Daly [6]	1954	1935–39	181	155–162	118–123	105–109
Projections to 1975:						
Cooke Commission [2]	1950	1945–49	190	132	134	119
Paley Commission [8]	1952	1948–50	193	133	133	118
Paley Commission * [8]	1952	1948–50	193	186	187	165
Cochrane and Lampe † [4]	1953	1935–39	190	169–177	125–135	113–120
Daly, Barton, and Rogers [6]	1956	1947–49	207	142	143	127
Ruttan [3]	1956	1950	221	160	162	143
Daly [6]	1957	1956	137	140–146	160–166	141–147
Daly and Barton [6]	1959	1947–49	137	162	164	145
Collins and Mehren † [7]	1958	1955	210–229	140–148	159–168	140–148
Projections to 1980:						
Senate Select Committee [9]	1960	1954	225–278	153–184	167–201	148–181
Land and Water Policy Committee [10]	1962	1959	261	146	183	161
Daly [6]	1963	1957–59	247–261	145–153	170–180	150–159
Projections to 2000:						
Senate Select Committee [9]	1960	1954	267–431	174–283	190–308	168–273

n.a. – not available.

* Represents a projection of attainable output rather than actual output.

† Projection for food output only, rather than total farm output.

[1] Joint Committee on Productive Capacity: U.S. Department of Agriculture, Land Grant Colleges—Department of Agriculture Joint Committee on Agricultural Productive Capacity, *Agriculture's Capacity to Produce: Possibilities Under Specified Conditions*, Agricultural Information Bulletin No. 88 (Washington: U.S. Government Printing Office, 1952).

[2] Cooke Commission: The President's Water Resources Policy Commission, *A Water Policy for the American People* (Washington: U.S. Government Printing Office, 1950), pp. 157–59.

(*Table footnotes continued on next page.*)

jections that the Census Bureau has compensated for its former tendency to produce conservative population projections.

Third, the more recent projections tend to project an output range based on alternative population, income, and demand assumptions rather than the single-point projections which characterize the earlier projections. This appears to reflect, in the main, efforts to hedge against future revisions in population and per capita income expectations.

When evaluated against the objective of accurate prediction, the farm output projections of the last decade are found to be seriously deficient. It is already clear that farm output in and during the next two decades will exceed any but the very latest projections.

Accurate prediction, as emphasized in Chapter 6, is not the only objective against which such projections should be evaluated. It is clearly not possible to predict the precise level of farm output for 1980 or any other future date. The actual level of farm output that will be achieved

---

[3] Ruttan: Vernon W. Ruttan, "The Contribution of Technological Change to Farm Output, 1950–75," *Review of Economics and Statistics*, Vol. 38 (February, 1956), pp. 64–65.

[4] Cochrane and Lampe: W. W. Cochrane and Harlen C. Lampe, "The Nature of the Race Between Food Supplies and Demand in the United States, 1951–75," *Journal of Farm Economics*, Vol. 35 (May, 1953), pp. 203–22.

[5] Black and Bonnen: J. D. Black and J. T. Bonnen, *A Balanced United States Agriculture in 1965*, National Planning Association Special Report No. 42 (Washington, 1956), pp. 7–10, 27.

[6] Daly and Associates: 1954—Rex F. Daly, "Some Considerations in Appraising the Long-Run Prospects for Agriculture," in *Long Range Economic Projection: Studies in Income and Wealth* (Princeton: Princeton University Press, 1954), Vol. 16, pp. 131–89. 1956—U.S. Department of Agriculture, *Farm Output, Past Changes and Projected Needs*, Agricultural Information Bulletin No. 162 (Washington: U.S. Government Printing Office, August, 1956), pp. 9 and 40. 1957—U.S. Joint Economic Committee, "Prospective Domestic Demand for Food and Fiber," in *Policy for Commercial Agriculture* (Washington: U.S. Government Printing Office, 1957), p. 111. 1959—Rex F. Daly and Glen T. Barton, "Prospects for Agriculture in a Growing Economy" in Earl O. Heady (ed.), *Problems and Policies of American Agriculture* (Ames: Iowa State University Press, 1959), p. 38. 1963—Rex F. Daly, "The National Environment for Business and Agriculture in the 1970's," paper presented at the Connecticut Cooperative Extension Conference, January 23, 1963, Storrs, Connecticut.

[7] Collins and Mehren: N. R. Collins and G. L. Mehren, "Demand Functions and Prospects," in *Agricultural Adjustment Problems in a Growing Economy*, edited by Earl O. Heady, Howard G. Diesslin, Harold R. Jensen, and Glenn L. Johnson (Ames: Iowa State College Press, 1958), p. 70.

[8] Paley Commission: The President's Materials Policy Commission, *Resources for Freedom: A Report to the President* (Washington: U.S. Government Printing Office, 1952), Vol. V, p. 66.

[9] Senate Select Committee: 1960—U.S. Department of Agriculture, *Land and Water Potentials and Future Requirements for Water*, United States Senate Select Committee on National Water Resources, 86th Congress, 2nd Session, Committee Print. No. 12 (Washington: U.S. Government Printing Office, 1960), pp. 22 and 27. The median projection for 1980 is 164 and for 2000 is 216.

[10] U.S.D.A. Land and Water Policy Committee: *Land and Water Resources: A Policy Guide*, U.S. Department of Agriculture (Washington, D.C., May, 1962), pp. 36, 37. The projections could also be classified under Daly and associates.

in 1980 will depend, to a substantial extent, on decisions that have not yet been made. The projections should be evaluated in terms of their contribution to policy decisions and not in terms of their accuracy as predictions. Their function in decision-making is to explore the empirical implications of alternative assumptions or courses of action. Decisions can then be made which will bring about the conditions leading to the desired results, or adjustments can be planned where sufficient control is not available.

Judged against this second objective, the national projections reviewed must receive an increasingly favorable evaluation. The more recent projections incorporate more completely the results of recent analytical work in the area of demand analysis and are based on population and income estimates that are considerably more sophisticated than the earlier estimates.

The national farm output projections which serve as a basis for the regional projections in Chapter 5 are shown in Table A3.2. All three assume an income elasticity of demand for food of 0.15, a 40 per cent rise in per capita income, a 2.5 per cent increase in per capita consumption of nonfood farm products, and a parity index of approximately 80. Projections I and II are based on an assumption that United States population will rise to approximately 260 million by 1980. This population will be realized if the 1955–57 level of fertility continues to 1980. In addition, projection I assumes the existence of agricultural surpluses at approximately current levels and no shift in the import-export picture with respect to agricultural products. Projection II assumes that by 1980 agricultural surpluses will decline to close to zero and that agricultural imports will rise slightly relative to exports. Projection III assumes that United States population will rise to 245 million by 1980. This implies a decline in fertility to the 1949–57 level. No reduction in surplus is assumed nor any shift in agricultural imports relative to exports.

In view of the tendency for recent farm output projections to fall short of actual output growth it seems reasonable to choose an output level near the upper end of the output range which now seems likely to prevail in a period centering on 1980. Projection I, with a consumption index of 165.6, seems to meet this specification fairly well. Furthermore, it approximates the projection of 164 (using 1954 = 100) made on the basis of similar population assumptions by the U.S. Department of

TABLE A3.2. Alternative Output Projections for United States Agriculture, 1980

Item	1955	1980
Population (millions)[1]		
Series II	165.3	260.0
Series III	165.3	245.4
Per-capita disposable income (dollars)[2]	1,641	2,300
Index of per capita income	100.0	140.2
Index of per-capita food consumption[3]	100.0	106.0
Series II projection		
Index of population	100.0	157.3
Index of aggregate food consumption	100.0	166.7
Index of consumption of nonfood farm products	100.0	161.2
Index of consumption of all farm products (I)	100.0	**165.6**
Adjustment for surplus disposal and imports	0.0	−4.8
Index of output requirements (II)	100.0	**160.8**
Series III projection		
Index of population	100.0	148.2
Index of aggregate food consumption	100.0	157.1
Index of consumption of nonfood farm products	100.0	151.0
Index of consumption of all farm products	100.0	155.9
Adjustment for surplus disposal and imports	0.0	0.0
Index of output requirements (III)	100.0	**155.9**

[1] Meyer Zitter and Jacob S. Siegel, "Illustrative Projections of the Population of the United States by Age and Sex: 1960 to 1980," *Current Population Reports,* U.S. Bureau of the Census Population Estimates, Series P–25, No. 187 (Washington: U.S. Government Printing Office, November 10, 1958), Table 1, p. 16.

[2] Per capita disposable personal income was obtained by dividing the total personal disposable income estimates for 1955 from Robert E. Graham, Jr., "Regional Income Distribution in 1957," *Survey of Current Business* (August, 1958), Table III, p. 12, by the census estimate of population in 1955. The per capita income estimate for 1980 is approximately the same as employed by Rex F. Daly and Glen T. Barton, "Prospects for Agriculture in a Growing Economy," in *Problems and Policies of American Agriculture* (Ames: Iowa State University Press, 1959), pp. 28–46. It is somewhat higher than employed by N. R. Collins and G. L. Mehren, "Demand Functions and Prospects," in *Agricultural Adjustment Problems in a Growing Economy,* edited by Earl O. Heady, Howard G. Diesslin, Harold R. Jensen, and Glenn L. Johnson (Ames: Iowa State College Press, 1958), p. 70.

[3] An income elasticity of demand of 0.15 for 1980 is assumed.

Agriculture for the Senate Select Committee on National Water Resources. Both projections are higher than the more recent projections adopted by the U.S.D.A. Land and Water Policy Committee in their report *Land and Water Resources: A Policy Guide,* and the more recent Daly projections (Table A3.1).

REGIONAL FARM OUTPUT PROJECTIONS

Only two comprehensive efforts to construct regional farm output projections have been identified. The projections arising from these studies are shown in Table A3.3.

TABLE A3.3. Two Regional Output Projections and Their Relation to National Farm Output Growth

Farm production region	U.S.D.A.-Land Grant College Joint Committee on Productive Capacity projection of attainable output [1]		Carter-Heady regional input-output study [2]	
	Projection to 1955	Relative to the United States	Projection to 1975	Relative to the United States
	1950=100		1954=100	
United States	120	same	128.0	same
Northeast	109	–	132.1	+
North Central	116	–	129.9	+
Corn Belt			130.4	+
Lake States			130.8	+
Northern Plains			127.2	–
South	125	+	124.5	–
Appalachia			131.3	+
Southeast			125.7	–
Delta			116.1	–
Southern Plains			121.0	–
Mountain	113	–	128.4	same
Pacific	109	–	128.2	same

[1] U.S. Department of Agriculture, Land Grant Colleges—Department of Agriculture Joint Committee on Agricultural Productive Capacity, *Agriculture's Capacity to Produce: Possibilities Under Specified Conditions,* Agricultural Information Bulletin No. 88 (Washington: U.S. Government Printing Office, 1952).

[2] Harold O. Carter and Earl O. Heady, *An Input-Output Analysis Emphasizing Regional and Commodity Sections of Agriculture,* Iowa Agricultural Experiment Station, Research Bulletin 469 (Ames, September, 1959), pp. 524–25.

In 1952, the U.S. Department of Agriculture published, under the auspices of a special Land Grant College–Department of Agriculture Joint Committee on Agricultural Productive Capacity, a report entitled *Agriculture's Capacity to Produce,* which included projections for 1955. The objective of the study was to estimate the production levels that farmers could attain over a four-to-five-year period under the pressures of an all-out production effort such as might be required in the event of a "hot" war. It was assumed that cost-price relationships would be favorable and that new technology would be exploited to the fullest extent possible.

A second set of regional output projections is available from a regional input-output study by Carter and Heady. Their projections assume a rise in utilization of farm products by the food-processing industry of 38 per cent between 1954 and 1975 and the continuation of 1954 production coefficients.

Because of the differences in the projection period only limited comparison between the two regional projections is possible. Two points are worth noting, however. First, the Land Grant Colleges–U.S. Department of Agriculture study projects a more rapid rise in farm output in the South than in the nation as a whole and a less rapid rise in farm output in the Mountain and Pacific regions than in the nation as a whole. The Carter-Heady projection, on the other hand, indicates, a more rapid rate of growth in farm output in the Northeast than in the nation as a whole. Second, it is rather interesting that the long-run Carter projections are based on fixed technical coefficients, which are best adapted for use in making short-run projections, while the Joint Committee assumed relatively complete use of new technology in making short-run projections.

A limited evaluation of the regional projections, based on the growth of farm output in each region relative to national farm output growth, is also possible. It is clear that the regional output growth patterns projected by the U.S.D.A. Joint Committee on Productive Capacity differ considerably from the patterns that actually obtained between 1947–49 and 1959 (see Table A3.4). The Committee projections indicate the smallest increases in output in the Northeast and the Pacific regions and the largest increases in the South. During the past decade the Pacific region has actually experienced the largest increase in output, while output in the three North Central regions has clearly expanded more rapidly than in the four regions of the South.

The principal discrepancies between the Carter projections and actual farm output between 1947–49 and 1959 are in the Northeast where the Carter projections imply a rise in output relative to the nation, in contrast to an actual decline in output relative to the nation, and in the Pacific region where the Carter projections indicate no change relative to the nation whereas actual output rose sharply relative to the nation. Within the South the Carter projections indicate the most rapid increase in output in the Appalachian region where actual output growth has expanded less rapidly than in any other region.

TABLE A3.4. Indexes of Farm Output for the United States and Major Farm Production Regions, 1950, 1954, and 1959

(1947–49 = 100)

Region	1950	1954 Index	1954 Relative to U.S. total	1959 Index	1959 Relative to U.S. total
United States	101	109		125	
Northeast	107	111	+	116	−
Corn Belt	104	117	+	134	+
Lake States	102	115	+	132	+
Northern Plains	103	98	−	118	−
Appalachia	98	106	−	110	−
Southeast	97	127	+	132	+
Delta	92	106	−	120	+
Southern Plains	89	96	−	118	−
Mountain	101	111	+	128	+
Pacific	105	121	+	131	+

Source: U.S. Department of Agriculture, *Changes in Farm Production and Efficiency,* Statistical Bulletin 233 (rev.) (Washington, D.C., September, 1962), p. 13.

The projection technique employed to estimate 1980 farm output in water resource regions for the demand model of this study is the "dampened trend" procedure first developed to project the regional distribution of population.[2] This procedure involves an assumption that the annual rate of change in each region's share of national farm output between some selected base year and the present will decline linearly to zero by some specified future period. In effect, this is an assumption that the forces which have brought about regional shifts in farm output during the base period are still in operation but that they will "play out" by the specified future date. This assumption is a major weakness of the "dampened trend" procedure. Although the forces which brought about changes in the regional distribution of farm output during the period 1925–29 to 1953–55 will likely become dampened during the next several decades, it seems fairly certain that other technological, economic, and institutional forces will come into existence and replace those that are now playing themselves out. To the extent that the new

[2] The "dampened trend" projection technique is described in Margaret J. Hagood and Jacob S. Siegel, "Projections of the Regional Distribution of the Population of the United States to 1975," *Agricultural Economics Research*, Vol. 3 (April, 1951), pp. 41–52. Also, Helen R. White, Jacob S. Siegel, and Beatrice M. Rosen, "Short Cuts in Computing Ratio Projections of Population," *Agricultural Economics Research,* Vol. 5 (January, 1953), pp. 5–11.

forces seriously reinforce or reverse present tendencies, the projections of the regional distribution of farm output based on dampened trends will be in error. The dampened trend procedure does, however, seem superior on logical grounds to any of the other simple projection techniques available. It would appear to be clearly superior, for example, to either of the following assumptions: (a) that each region would account for the same share of national farm output as in some past period, or (b) that each region's share will continue to rise or decline at the same rate as during some past period.

Farm output estimates are not available by water resource regions. Projections have therefore been made on the basis of the value of farm products sold. Tables A3.5—A3.7 show the value of farm products sold in each water resource region for 1929, 1939, and 1954 and projections for 1980 in dollars, as a percentage of total U.S. farm sales, and as indexes of farm sales. In all three tables the data for 1929, 1939, and 1954 are presented in current dollar values; the dollar value projections to 1980 are in terms of 1954 prices and reflect changes in "real" output.

The projection technique employed by the Department of Agriculture in its report to the Senate Select Committee on National Water Resources involved the projection of the value of crop and pasture production rather than the value of total farm output or sales. A direct comparison of the output levels assumed in the report to the Select Committee and in this analysis is, therefore, not possible. It is possible, however, from the data presented in Table A3.7 to obtain some insight into the extent of agreement or disagreement in the two projections.

The dampened trend projection used in this study indicates more rapid expansion of farm output in the western water resource regions and less rapid expansion of farm output in the eastern water resource regions than the crop and pasture production projections of the Department. Within the East, the greatest disagreement appears in the Lower Arkansas-White-Red water resource region. For this region, the Department projections indicate more rapid growth than for the East as a whole, while the dampened trend projections indicate less rapid growth than for the East as a whole. In the West, the greatest discrepancies appear in the three Pacific regions and the Colorado River region. The dampened trend projection indicates more rapid growth in these regions than in the

West as a whole, while the Department projections indicate less rapid growth. Important discrepancies also appear in the Western Gulf and Upper Arkansas-White-Red water resource regions where dampened trend projections indicate slower growth and the Department projections indicate more rapid growth than in the West as a whole.

TABLE A3.5. Farm Sales in Water Resource Regions, 1929, 1939, 1954, and Projected to 1980 [1]

(million $)

Water resource regions	1929	1939	1954	1980
Western:				
Pacific Northwest	467.8	329.0	1,173.4	2,004.2
Central Pacific	410.2	329.9	1,585.9	3,402.5
South Pacific	188.5	125.3	579.4	1,091.8
Colorado River	130.2	95.9	533.8	1,168.6
Great Basin	91.8	59.6	170.4	248.4
Upper Rio Grande and Pecos	83.9	70.5	232.7	418.4
Western Gulf	601.3	418.4	1,406.6	2,316.9
Upper Arkansas-White-Red	590.8	321.8	948.3	1,284.5
Upper Missouri River	1,464.1	788.9	2,964.0	4,527.6
Total, West	4,028.6	2,539.3	9,594.5	16,462.9
Eastern:				
Northeast	1,035.2	780.9	2,056.0	3,152.0
Great Lakes	860.5	661.0	1,788.2	2,799.5
Corn Belt	2,943.9	2,288.4	6,892.7	11,487.2
Southeast	1,218.6	905.5	2,286.4	3,398.9
Florida	92.0	88.9	466.1	1,162.5
Lower Mississippi River	396.1	279.2	903.8	1,486.6
Lower Arkansas-White-Red	435.4	270.4	650.5	859.2
Total, East	6,981.8	5,274.3	15,043.7	24,345.9
U.S. Total	11,010.3	7,813.6	24,638.2	40,808.8

[1] Current dollar value for 1929, 1939, and 1954; projections for 1980 are in terms of 1954 prices and reflect changes in "real" output.

TABLE A3.6. Share of States in U.S. Farm Sales in Water Resource Regions, 1929, 1939, 1954, and Projected to 1980

(Per cent)

Water resource regions	1929	1939	1954	1980
Western:				
Pacific Northwest	4.248	4.210	4.761	4.911
Central Pacific	3.726	4.222	6.444	8.337
South Pacific	1.712	1.604	2.351	2.675
Colorado River	1.182	1.227	2.166	2.863
Total	2.894	2.831	4.517	5.539
Great Basin	.834	.762	.691	.609
Upper Rio Grande and Pecos	.762	.902	.944	1.025
Western Gulf	5.461	5.354	5.708	5.677
Upper Arkansas-White-Red	5.366	4.118	3.848	3.147
Upper Missouri River	13.297	10.096	12.028	11.094
Total, West	36.588	32.495	38.941	40.340
Eastern:				
Northeast	9.402	9.994	8.353	7.724
Great Lakes	7.815	8.460	7.256	6.860
Corn Belt	26.738	29.288	27.971	28.148
Southeast	11.069	11.589	9.281	8.328
Florida	.836	1.138	1.891	2.849
Lower Mississippi River	3.597	3.573	3.667	3.643
Lower Arkansas-White-Red	3.955	3.461	2.640	2.105
Total, East	63.412	67.503	61.059	59.660
U.S. Total	100.00	99.998	100.00	100.00

TABLE A3.7. Indexes of Value of Farm Sales in Water Resource Regions, 1929, 1939, 1954, and Projected to 1980, Compared with Value of Crop and Pasture Production Projected by U.S.D.A.

(1954 = 100)

Water resource regions	Farm sales 1929	Farm sales 1939	Farm sales 1954	Farm sales 1980	Crop and pasture production 1980
Western:					
Pacific Northeast	39.9	28.0	100	170.8	123
Central Pacific	25.8	20.8	100	214.3	124
South Pacific	32.5	21.6	100	188.4	125
Colorado River	24.4	18.0	100	218.9	123
Great Basin	53.9	35.0	100	145.8	122
Upper Rio Grande and Pecos	36.1	30.3	100	179.8	142
Western Gulf	42.7	29.7	100	164.7	173
Upper Arkansas-White-Red	62.3	33.9	100	135.5	155
Upper Missouri River	49.4	26.6	100	152.8	127
Total, West	42.0	26.5	100	171.6	137
Eastern:					
Northeast	50.3	37.9	100	153.1	125
Great Lakes	48.1	37.0	100	156.6	122
Corn Belt	42.7	33.2	100	166.7	139
Southeast	53.3	39.6	100	148.6	151 (Southeast and Florida combined)
Florida	19.7	19.1	100	249.4	
Lower Mississippi River	43.8	30.9	100	164.5	164
Lower Arkansas-White-Red	66.9	41.6	100	132.1	172
Total, East	46.4	35.1	100	161.8	141
U.S. Total	44.7	31.7	100	165.6	140

INDEX

(f) refers to Figures (t) refers to Tables

AUTHOR INDEX

THE ECONOMIC DEMAND FOR IRRIGATED ACREAGE:
New Metholodogy and Some Preliminary Projections, 1954–1980

by Vernon W. Ruttan

designer:	Athena Blackorby
typesetter:	Baltimore Type and Composition Corp.
typefaces:	Times Roman, Bodoni 375
printer:	The John D. Lucas Printing Co.
paper:	Perkins and Squier GM
binder:	Moore and Company
cover material:	Columbia Riverside Linen